CW00407334

INITIATION

Your breakfast bagel did not just materialize. The wheat had to be planted, tended, harvested, hulled and ground.

And our men and women that sacrifice everything for us: Our soldiers, teachers, doctors, nurses, police and firefighters and especially mothers and fathers—they were forged straight and strong, sharp and resilient, for their impossible tasks ahead, in the crucible of life. All the fruits of life come from labor.

Boys and girls are born. Men and women are trained.

"This book is a great read! It is entertaining and full of ancient teachings that offer practical life advice for today. For more than eighteen years I have experienced personally, and witnessed in others, the changes in life that result when people practice the techniques described in this book."
—**Darin Ashley**, Major, USMC (Ret)

"This book and its teaching have helped me to answer the eternal questions of 'why am I here, what is my purpose?' An invaluable skill considering we are living in a time when children are killing themselves because they have no definable reason to live."
—**Christa Ashley**

"As essential as water—a handbook for the human race."
—**Dr. Joseph K. Eleid**, M.D.

"With compelling clarity and courage, Jeffrey Prather offers a hopeful prescription for those poised in the search for purpose and truth. **Initiation** has seamlessly brought together that rare combination of entertainment and enlightenment in a memoir that seems destined to take its place alongside best-selling authors like Dan Millman. This is a piercing book that may change the lives of those who endeavor to read it."
—**Louis Breton**, Founder, ARC Technologies

"**Initiation** is a story of learning—not so much through someone else's particular way, but simply by coming to realize how things may really work; by coming to accept who we really are. And once understanding occurs—the choices and the decisions that lay before each of us are revealed."
—**Charles Rutta**

"I read this book with great curiosity and interest because my husband is a Navajo spiritual teacher. The Navajo are close cousins to the Apache and our son-in-law is an Apache. Evocative of the Carlos Castaneda books, I found this book to be simple, sincere and full of wonderful teachings."
—**Teddi Tsosie**, Spirit Visions: The Old Ones Speak

INITIATION

Boys Are Born,
Men Are Trained

*My Journey with
an Apache Medicine Man*

JEFFREY PRATHER

Blue Dolphin Publishing

Copyright © 2011 Jeffrey Prather
All rights reserved.

Published by Blue Dolphin Publishing, Inc.
P.O. Box 8, Nevada City, CA 95959
Orders: 1-800-643-0765
Web: www.bluedolphinpublishing.com

ISBN: 978-1-57733-254-1 paperback
ISBN: 978-1-57733-331-9 e-book

Library of Congress Cataloging-in-Publication Data

Prather, Jeffrey Lynn.
   Initiation : boys are born, men are trained / Jeffrey Prather.
      p. cm.
   Includes bibliographical references and index.
   ISBN 978-1-57733-254-1 (pbk. : alk. paper)
    1. Prather, Jeffrey Lynn. 2. Apache philosophy. 3. Conduct of life.
I. Title.
   E99.A6P73 2010
   170'.44--dc22

                                                              2010044922

Cover photo: Courtesy of Author

Printed in the United States of America

5   4   3   2   1

For *Besh Koon*, the Broken Arrow, last of the great *Diyin*.
I hope I have done you justice. *Shi'i okahi'i.*

CONTENTS

PREFACE

THIS IS A STORY based on real events. But it is not a story of the Apache way. This is a story of one extraordinary Apache's way that was so limitless in profundity that he transcended his own culture's spiritual boundaries. And in his genius, he taught me to transcend mine. Included herein are elements that every Apache will recognize and none will. The same goes for the non-Native student of spirituality. The point is not to own it, but to share it. So here it is. For all my relations.

ACKNOWLEDGMENTS

MANY THANKS to my most lovely and patient wife Rachel, my kids, Jess, Evan and Isabel, who embody the best of me, and my wonderful parents—all of them, also to Pansy, Patsy, Eddie, Jonell, Steve, Carol, Myron and the boys (now men), and everybody else up at San Carlos, Bylas and White Mountain who welcomed me without question, then fed me, sang with me and just generally and generously put up with me. Lastly, my profound thanks to Paul and Nancy Clemens, who immediately heard, understood, and answered the call. Without their vision and commitment, this book would not be.

SHOWING UP

The first thing is always to show up. If you don't show up,
nothing else can ever happen. You have to show up,
whether you want to or not, whether you are welcome or
expected or not—whether you even know why.
Then you have to keep showing. Every day, every week,
every month, every year. Rain or shine.
And there are always a thousand reasons not to show.
—JRP

THE SIGN ABOVE THE DOOR READ:
"DESERT SOL, INDIAN MOCCASINS AND JEWELRY"
in big, white block letters. A faded, but full-color high-top moccasin jutted up and out from the horizontal lettering and past the
sign edge itself, the buckskin tan leggings sharp against the deep
ocean blue of the Tucson sky. It was the spring of 1978, and I had
found it.

Ever since I could remember, I had been fascinated by
American Indian culture, especially the Apache. There was just
something about their wild and fierce, free ways that fascinated
the Midwest boy that I still was. I was raised in Cincinnati but sum-
mered out West with my folks, and on trips as a child had tasted
the reservation experience. Two years at the University of Dayton
was all the gray dull sameness that I could stomach.

I transferred out to the University of Arizona my junior year.
Back then the college and the town still held an exotic atmosphere
of the old West. I loved to get off campus every chance I got and
prowl the city's back streets and explore its secrets. Tucson was

1

still small, at least well under a million, and the big city had yet to vanquish the frontier feel of the place. Around town at night you still spotted a Stetson alongside glossy black Indian braids, amidst the ball caps and college T-shirts.

I discovered Old Tucson, which I recognized from a dozen old westerns, the Desert Museum, San Xavier Mission, and other lesser known places such as *El Tiradito*, the old shrine where the ground was solid wax from the years of candles offered there to the tragic but mysterious love triangle memorialized in crumbling adobe.

Shortly thereafter I heard about a shop that built traditional Indian moccasins. Someone I ran into at the student union—I forget who, had told me about the place. Cruising Speedway just north of the University of Arizona, with my convertible's top down, the sign had popped almost magically into view overhead.

I pulled in right in front of the front door underneath the signage, parked and got out. I jerked the screen door open and the metal handle seared itself into the flesh of my right hand. I shifted my grasp to the relatively cool metal knob of the carved inner wooden door and entered.

"You're late."

I stepped into the darkened room, not even sure of what I might have just heard. The white-hot sunlight of the Arizona day had left me temporarily blind and disoriented. I stopped just inside the doorway, my left hand still on the door knob, trying to get my bearings. My right hand fingers still burned.

"He said, 'You are late'."

The room was long, cool and dark. I began to make out a glass counter running the length of the show room. Under the glass, thousands of pieces of Hopi and Zuni silverwork set with blue turquoise and red coral gleamed on black velvet. Conical Apache baskets hung from the peeled wood *vigas* in the ceiling, dangling long fringe tipped with glittering tin cones that gently swung in the breeze from the open door. They made a soft, pleasant tinkling sound that somehow emphasized the quiet of the place even more. Red, white, black and gray Navajo blankets adorned the burnt orange Saltillo tile floor, and more were folded carefully and piled high on a carved Mexican mahogany table. Further back, I could just make out a display table of various moccasin types in every natural shade of leather imaginable. I sensed, more than saw, two figures leaning against the counter.

"Talking to me, sir?" I replied, unsure which, if anyone, had addressed me.

As my eyes adjusted to the relative darkness of the room, I could make out two men, one in front of the counter leaning against it and the other behind it and leaning on it.

The man on the far side rested both elbows on the glass. But the near man leaned sideways against it with only one forearm on it. I was young and polite from my many years in a military-style dojo, and I automatically addressed just about everyone as "sir."

"See anybody else in here?" The man in front was suddenly standing straight, although I had somehow not seen him straighten, even though my eyes had never left him. I was puzzling over the strangeness of his movement or rather the lack of it when I realized that he was addressing me again.

"Both blind and deaf and on both sides, and late to boot. How you ever gonna keep up?"

He was tall, lean and dark, and clearly a Native American full-blood. He was dressed simply in the Western fashion of the day: faded blue Levis, worn, pointed cowboy boots, oval silver buckle and white, long-sleeved snap shirt. His hair was short but still mostly black with grey streaks, even though he must have been in to his sixties. His cheekbones were high, his epicanthic eyelids hooded so that only a little of his brown eyes were visible, and his ears noticeably large. He wrapped himself in the solitude of a regal dignity, like a blanket. It was an air around him that was impossible to ignore and almost palpable to the touch.

Not knowing what else to say and feeling awkward in the silence I said, "How are you?"

I realized he was smiling slightly as he shook his head slowly from side to side. There was something about him that fixed my attention yet somehow altered it. It was as if I was on some kind of time delay and he wasn't.

"Looking and seeing, hearing and listening—you?" His eyes were bright against the brown wrinkle of his face.

"Me what?" I said.

He just stared at me for a long moment as if waiting for me to say something else. Then he smiled and turned towards the man behind the counter. He pursed his lips and kind of pointed with a slight nod of his chin.

"When those are ready, have him drop them off to me at my place."

"Yes, sir." It was the man behind the counter. He too had suddenly straightened. I found it a little strange that he too had "sirred" the tall Indian. He was white and in his mid-thirties with mussed, neck length, dirty blonde hair.

I heard the door close and realized that he had done it again. He was gone and I had not even seen him move towards the door.

"Well?"

I turned back towards the man behind the counter.

"Well what?" Now I was totally confused.

"What are you going to do?" He was smiling now and seeming to enjoy my disorientation.

"About?"

"These." He held up the longest pair of high-top moccasins I had ever seen. They were a rich buckskin color just like the horse. The soles were hard, white rawhide, but cracked and worn through at the balls of the feet. They curled up into the distinctive toe piece that I recognized at once as Chiricauhua Apache. My heart beat just a bit faster.

"Looks like I found what I was looking for," I said slowly.

"More like the other way around." The guy behind the counter was actually laughing.

"You laughing at me?" I was angry. I was an accomplished black belt, had placed high in several recent, national matches and was used to respect, not mocking. I also took myself pretty seriously back then.

"No, Phillip always has this affect on folks." He crossed his arms sizing me up. "So what are you going to do?"

"Who are you and what the hell are you talking about?" My voice rose with my temper and I took a step forward. The soft shopkeeper finally looked afraid. I felt gratified.

"Whoa, partner. Slow down there. Don't do violence to an old hippie now. I'm Steve, I'm the owner." He extended his right hand while patting the air with his left. I shook back.

"Okay, Steve the owner, nice to meet you. I'm Jeff . Now once again, what are you talking about and who is Phillip?"

"You just met him, son, Phillip Talgo. Big time Apache medicine man, son and grandson of Chiricauhua chiefs, blood relative of Cochise, radio DJ up on San Carlos—KNDE, Harvard grad, army vet, yada yada yada. And just like every other Indian— always broke, always after a hand-out, never pays his bills. But looks like he's going to get you to do it—aren't you?"

My head spun. Numerous dots in my life seemed to be suddenly and dramatically connecting. Since I was a kid, I had known I was adopted. I was lucky. I got out of Saint Joseph's orphanage very young, adopted by a wonderful, Catholic-Baptist couple in Cincinnati that had loved and nurtured me with nothing but the best: private schools, vacations in Europe and summers out West.

Like all kids back then I played cowboys and Indians and had admired the Indian mystique of wild freedom and fierce living. But even as an adult I was still somehow drawn to native peoples and in particular the Apache. All American Indians had been formidable fighters. But the Apache were the toughest of the tough. And the legendary Chiricahua were the last to succumb to the U.S. Army—actually the Apache scouts, since even the hardiest American soldiers could never keep up. They were the Spartans of the old West, and I had longed my whole life to meet them. Like Lawrence, Houston and Jeffords before me, some part of me was somehow quantitatively connected to the desert and viscerally attached to its people. It was the real, but secret reason I had transferred out West. But I had never actually told anyone this.

Somehow I felt connected to them. I secretly believed my birth mother was Indian. There was no rational reason for this. I just felt it every day. My adopted dad somehow always sensed this in me. Perhaps he was extra-sensitive, since I was his first adopted child. But he took me to reservations, gave me books about Indians, and told me their stories. He had even pulled me out of Summit

Country Day one afternoon to go home early and watch his favorite movie, *Apache* with Burt Lancaster.

"Hey, you still there?" Steve waved his hand in front of my face and snapped his fingers.

"You don't think much of him?" I asked.

"He's Indian. Drunk, broke or both. But looks like he hooked you with his noble red man routine. Wanna buy one of his tapes?" Steve held up a tape of Apache music with Phillip's name on it.

"Why'd you sir him then," I continued.

"What?" Steve was arranging jewelry inside the main case.

"If he's such a nothing loser, then why did you say, 'yes, sir'?" I asked again.

"I have no idea what you are talking about." I just stared at him. Either he was lying or he just didn't remember. At any rate it didn't seem worth pursuing. Maybe he was so difficult to talk to because he had been a stoned-out hippie. Too many drugs. Maybe that was it.

The screen door slammed and the inner door creaked. A couple of over-weight, middle-aged, tourist women came in wearing child-like pink and red cowboy hats.

"Morning, ladies, looking for the best Indian jewelry in Tucson?" Steve moved to the ladies as they gushed over Navajo squash blossom necklaces. I hesitated, then headed for the door. I waved at Steve.

"See ya."

"Excuse me just a minute, ladies. Here, try these on, they're from Third Mesa. Hey, hold up there, Jim."

"Jeff, it's Jeff."

"Yeah, okay. So are you going pay for these or what?" He held up the Apache moccasins.

"What is with you and these moccasins?"

"I'm a businessman. I like to make money. The sixties commune thing didn't work out, so now I'm a capitalist."

"My God, it's like talking to my mother." I was just about at the end of my rope with this guy. "Why me and these mocs?"

"He told you to." Steve rolled his eyes.

"To what?" I rolled mine too.

"What are you, deaf? Ladies, I'll be right there. Just a minute more. Look, kid, remember Phillip said you'd pay for the repair of the soles of the moccasins?"

"Actually, no, I don't."

"Well, he did. Then he told you to deliver them to his place when they were done. Now do you remember?" I thought hard for a minute as I watched the red and pink cowboy hats bob up and down. It was a surreal moment. I felt like I was in a movie but without the script.

"Yeah, I guess so. But why me?"

"Who knows why Indian witch doctors do whatever. But he actually came in early this morning—was outside before I even opened up. He's been waiting on you all week."

I stopped and turned. My stomach flipped like I was on a roller coaster.

"What do you mean all week?"

"I mean he's been waiting for you all week, since Monday. He's been talking about you, how inconsiderate you are making him wait three days. I mean, it is Wednesday. Even on Indian time that's pretty bad." My skin tingled.

"But I never met him before. I never even knew this shop was here," I protested.

"Look, I've got customers. Yes or no, are you going to pay for 'em or not?"

I was stunned. Time was slowing all around me. Everything was in slow motion but in magnified detail. I could see Steve's lips still moving.

"Yeah, okay, I'll pay for 'em," I finally said.

"Great, come back on Saturday afternoon. See ya then. Okay, ladies, shall I wrap both of those up for you?" Steve was already back to his customers.

I turned away, pushed open the doors and stumbled out. The white hot sunshine stabbed into my eyes temporarily blinding me yet again. Then the Arizona heat hit me like a hammer.

"Both blind and deaf and on both sides, and late to boot. How you ever gonna keep up?"

Keeping up with all our responsibilities as real men is overwhelming. That's one reason why so many guys abdicate their duties and run around acting like spoiled brat boys.

If you are the latter, you're probably not ready to read this book and you should return it for some of your favorite comic books, and no, I'm not going to call them graphic novels.

However, if you are interested in changing—growing—becoming the man those who rely on you need you to be, then you'll need to recognize your teachers. I didn't recognize my teacher when we first met.

To recognize your teachers, start to see instead of just look.

Listen instead of just hear.

Then start to listen and see those around you.

You don't need to go out to Arizona. Start in your own home. With your own family.

See what those closest to you can teach you.

See what your relationship to those around you really is, not what you have defined it as.

Listen, without predisposition, to what they have to say to you.

The only thing we can change is ourselves. But when we change, our relationship to the world around us changes. And then, just a little, the world changes too.

8

HEEDING THE CALL

Most don't even believe there is call, so they never listen.
A smaller group believes but doesn't listen, and thus
never hear it. A few then hear but can't believe
what they are hearing and so ignore it. An even smaller number
don't ignore it, but can't understand it. Still fewer understand,
but in understanding find the call too inconvenient, difficult or
downright scary. In the end only one or two of the bravest
or most foolish, pay heed.

—JRP

I WENT BACK TO DESERT SOL that Saturday afternoon. Steve wasn't there but his mom Daisy was. She was much nicer than him and we hit it off right away. But unfortunately she had no idea where the moccasins were. I got a good look around the store though as we searched together. Despite Steve's attitude the stuff was all authentic Native made and of the highest quality—real Hopi inlay, true Navajo weavings and authentic Apache baskets. No new age mandalas or fake dream catchers that in the bad old days were actually scalp stretchers. I was impressed and said so.

"Steve has a lot of great stuff here," I said.

"Oh yes, he's always been quite the traveler. He knows everybody on the reservations up north. He even used to travel to Thailand and Viet Nam back in the sixties, looking for antiques."

"Was he in the military?" I asked.

"Lord no, he just likes to see the world and buy antiques and knick-knacks."

9

"Is there a number where we can reach him?" I asked. Dutifully Daisy went through her phone list. She even tried their own house, but no one answered.

"How about a number for Phillip?"

She shook her head emphatically. "No, no, Phillip doesn't have a phone, at least not that I know of."

"Well, thanks," I said and pushed out.

"Why don't you come back on Monday?" She waved me out the door.

I did come back on Monday but the store was inexplicably closed. I was busy with school until I recalled the moccasins and returned to the store on the following Saturday. Steve was there. But the mocs were still not resoled. After another disjointed, rambling conversation I learned that Steve's cobbler, an old Vietnamese man that he had met on his travels, was out sick and had not yet finished the task.

"Well, do you have a number Phillip can be reached at?" I asked in exasperation.

"Nope," Steve said slowly.

"How about an address then?" I asked, trying to keep my temper in check. But Steve didn't reply.

"Well?" I nearly shouted at him.

"Steven, you behave and give Jeffrey Phillip's address right now."

Steve's mom had appeared over his shoulder. The look on Steve's face was a cross between a patient getting a colonoscopy and polio shot all at once. It was an expression that I would see repeated year after year, decade after decade in my long friendship with Steve, and one I would never tire of seeing.

"Yeah, Steve," I chimed in, earning a look from Steve's mom, "Just trying to be helpful, ma'am." She smiled and shook her head.

"But then I'll never get paid for these things, mom," he winced and whined while simultaneously holding up the mocs as evidence. "You know how those Indians are."

But his mom had already headed to the back of the store. Steve rolled his eyes and muttered under his breath.

"What was that?" I replied innocently.

"I said you really should pay for these first." Steve held up the mocs. They really were beautiful.

"Here smell that." He tossed me the moccasins. I caught them but didn't move.

"Smell 'em!" Steve shouted now.

"Okay, okay." I raised them cautiously to my nose and was rewarded with a rich, smoky aroma.

"Genuine Indian brain tan, nothing like that in modern chemical hides."

I ran my finger over the surface. The grain of the deer hide was light, almost feathery. When I ran my finger across it, the grain changed, leaving a shimmering trace of my fingers. The mocs themselves were light-weight but strong, and the texture of the skin was a rich, buttery buckskin. White clay swirls and dusty yellow stains fascinated the eye to follow them into their depth. The white rawhide soles stood out against the sunshine yellow of the buckskin. They curled up around the sides and the soles of the feet and looked like they would provide considerable protection from the cactus-filled desert. The rawhide toe piece turned up into a white disc over the big toe and was a little larger than a silver dollar.

"No, Steve, I shouldn't pay for these first. But you should do what you're told too and give me Phillip's address." I chuckled. "What's this toe thing anyway?"

"Who knows, who cares, and what the hell do you want to get involved with that crazy old Indian for anyway? He's just a scammer. He'll just take you for a ride with all that Apache warrior crap. Just like he scammed the Kennedys."

"The Kennedys—as in President?" I asked, genuinely surprised. Steve scowled and threw up his hands.

"Oh, please God, not you too. Yeah, the Kennedys—the entire crooked clan. They all flew in to see him. Like he was some kind of national treasure or something. He sings a couple of war songs, does a rain dance, everybody oohs and aahs and he rakes it in."

I picked up a record album cover that read, *The Apache Day in Song* by Phillip Talgo. It was a double containing four vinyl LPs. I put that back and picked up a cassette tape by Phillip as well.

"Seems like he's some kind of singer." I held up the cassette case.

"What's this on the cover?" I asked pointing to a bunch of black and white painted figures wearing fantastic white and black painted wooden headdresses, holding wooden swords and clad in Apache high-top mocs.

"Apache devil dancers. Yeah, you should buy those—they're great. You know Ted Nugent goes up there to San Carlos to bow hunt, and he says Phillip is a great singer and he ought to know. Want 'em? Here's another great set." Steve had turned his sales-man mode on me, sensing my interest, and he was, though I hate to admit it, difficult to resist.

"Will you give me Phillip's address if I do?" I countered.

"If you buy the set, I'll take you there," he sighed in exaspera-tion.

"It's a deal," I said, feeling like I had somehow just bought a used car. I paid for the music. "Okay, let's go." The shop door opened and in walked a gaggle of tourists talking among them-selves in some foreign tongue.

"Germans!" Steve whispered and scooted over to the crowd. "Germans love Indian stuff!"

"What about our deal?" I objected.

Steve threw up his hands and yelled from across the room, "Can't go now. Tyndall down Campbell, the unit on the end. Good morning, folks, how can I help you?"

"That's right around the corner! Why didn't you just tell me?" I yelled. All the Germans looked at me in silence. Steve smiled back.

"I'm a businessman. Nobody gets something for nothing, kid." Steve disappeared into his crowd of customers. I shook my head, waved my bag of newly purchased music in his general direction and walked out.

I drove over to Tyndall. At the dead end of the street was a small, low, run-down duplex. Beyond it, as in many parts of Tuc-son, the town ran out and the desert returned. There must have been a stream not far away because several beautiful, giant cotton woods sighed in the breeze, filling the air with the little tufts they were named after.

I figured that it must be the red brick apartment on the far end. It was only fifteen minutes away from Steve's, but the trees created a wall of solitude that isolated the place from the bustle of Speedway. I knocked on the screen door. No answer. After seconds I knocked again. Still no answer. I cupped my hands and peered inside.

The inner door was open, so I could see inside through the screen. On the cheap kitchen table was a kind of make-shift drum—a coffee can with a buckskin stretched over it, held in place by what looked like a bicycle inner tube. Sitting on top of the skin was a skinny wooden drum stick curved into a circle on one end. The other end was wrapped in a buckskin strip.

It was clear no one was home. Evidently I was in the right place at the wrong time. I went back to my car and put in Phillip's tape. The music was a drum and a bell, the voice evidently Phillip's.

The music was guttural, powerful and primordial. It was different than the high-pitched shrieking songs of the Plains Indian music that I had heard at powwows. In mid-song each one switched to a chant in Apache, which I guessed was telling a story and I was desperately curious to translate. The songs seemed ancient and echoed against something deep inside me. The music somehow fixed my attention, and I lost track of time. The sun dropped and drenched the dash in gold as it set. After the cycle of songs restarted, I started to tap my hand on the Fiat's steering wheel and attempted to sing along.

I picked up the cassette and stared at the strange figures on the cover, trying to understand the meaning behind their elaborate dress. Eventually I let my eyes close and leaned my head back against the rest. I continued to sing or rather tried to. Then I must have drifted off.

"Uh huh."

I jumped in my seat smacking my head on the low roof as I opened my eyes. Phillip's face filled the driver side window.

"Ow. How long you been there?" I rubbed the top of my head which only made it worse. I winced.

"That is without a doubt the worst singing I have ever heard." He stood up and towered over my tiny X-1-9 sports car. His head shook slowly, and then deadpan he pointed with pursed lips towards a nearby mesquite.

"Two gophers just dropped dead over there your singin' so bad." Inadvertently I looked. "You know I think they might be on the endangered species list." He turned and walked towards the apartment door. "Still can't figure why *we* aren't though."

"Hey, wait a minute," I yelled. "I been waiting for you all afternoon."

"So what? I been waiting on you for years," he said over his shoulder.

"So where are you going? Let's talk then." I opened the car door and stood up.

"Where's my *keiban?*"

"Your what?"

"Moccasins, where are my moccasins?" He sounded like he was talking to a child.

"They're not ready yet," I admitted.

"Then come back with them when they are." He walked in the door and shut it behind him.

I just stood there. Finally I got up the nerve to walk over. I knocked three times and waited. No answer. I knocked again and waited. From inside I began to hear drumming and singing. He was in there drumming and singing while I stood out here! Or was it a record? I knocked again.

The door opened just as I was about to knock again. He just looked at me eyebrows raised. "Yes?"

"Yes, what?" I replied.

"You're the one knockin'." He did that little point at me with his chin.

"Well, yes sir, I did drive over here to see you and been waiting all afternoon."

"We already had that discussion. Unless you wanna talk woman. You aren't a girly-boy are you?"

"No, sir! I'm not a girl-boy and I'm not a boy. I'm a grown man—all man, I'm a black belt," I inserted forcefully. I was young and muscular, with nothing gay about me. "Why do you ask?"

"You're repeating yourself the way women do when they talk at each other, to make an emotional point instead of a rational one—to reassure each other and themselves. And you're grown all right, but I am not so sure about your manhood."

I opened my mouth to protest this latest nonsense, but he cut me off with a raised hand.

"*Keiban*. Come back when you got 'em." He shut the door.

I stood there trying to decipher the conversation. He wasn't angry or even impatient. He just seemed to be operating on a different set of rules I didn't know.

After a couple of minutes the sound of singing and drumming from inside resumed. I thought about knocking but somehow knew he wouldn't answer, so I got in my car and drove off, Phillip's songs still playing on my tape deck. Clearly I had to recalibrate.

"So what? I been waiting on you for years."

So you have shown up. Congratulations. You are probably late. I was.

You have started to see those around you, and what your actual interaction with them really is.

You are starting to listen to what those around you are really saying to you, not just with their words, but most importantly with their actions.

Now figure out who is waiting on you.

And for what?

What have they come to expect from you?

But what should they expect from you?

If there is a difference between what they have come to expect and what they actually expect, is that difference negative or positive?

If the difference is positive, congratulations!

If the difference is negative, be honest.

Decide how you will make up the difference.

Don't bother telling anyone you are going to make up the difference.

They won't believe you. Anyway why should they?

Just do it.

PAYING THE DEBT

The debt is always expensive and never what you imagined.
—JRP

TWO WEEKS LATER I got a break from the demands of school and showed back up at Desert Sol. It was open and Steve was there. I almost fainted in surprise.

"Where you been? The mocs have been ready for weeks," Steve asked in total sincerity as he plopped the moccasins on the glass counter. I rolled my eyes and picked them up.

The soles were new and thick and a fresh snow white that was a wonderful, eye-pleasing complement to the creamy buckskin uppers. The toe pieces were a little larger and, unlike the old ones, stuck up straight up, ensuring that the wearer would trip almost immediately.

"Shouldn't these be down?" I asked pointing to the toe pieces.

"Step on 'em," Steve replied. I dropped them to the store floor.

"Wait up, man. First off, you haven't paid for those yet. Second, you do that while you're wearing 'em."

"Why do I have to pay? They're not even mine," I asked.

"He said you were slow too," Steve murmured. I stared at him.

"What are you talking about now?" I snapped. Steve seemed to bring out the worst of my temper—and enjoyed doing it.

"When Phillip was in here waiting for you, he said you were not only late but slow. Years late and years slow. I don't get why he likes you so much."

17

"Whaddya mean, 'likes me so much'?" Now I was totally confused. "He wouldn't even let me in his place. And how could he like me when he doesn't even know me?"

"I don't know." Steve rolled his eyes. "Never heard him talk about anybody so much. You rich?"

"No, I'm not rich," I snorted.

"Pretty fancy little Italian sports car though." Steve looked out the window. "Bet your dad bought it for you." In fact my dad had bought it for me, which really ticked me off.

"That must be the con. You're rich like the Kennedys. Bet you're Catholic too." In point of fact I was Catholic. Steve had hooked me, knew it, and was slowly reeling me in while jerking the line to create as much pain and stress as possible.

"So what?"

"So two hundred bucks," Steve demanded.

"You're crazy." There was no way I was going to let Steve take me for a ride.

"One seventy five," Steve shot back.

"Where's your mom, in the back? Daisy!" I called out loudly.

"Okay, okay, hold on." Steve grimaced, scratched his ear, and rubbed his neck. "A hundred and twenty five."

"A hundred," I said with surprising finality.

Steve looked like he was drinking sour milk. I put a hundred dollar bill on the counter. Just then Steve's mom came out from the back of the store.

"Hi, ma'am," I smiled and waved cheerfully.

"Well, hello there, Jeffrey, it's great to see you," she waved back. Steve snatched the hundred up. I nodded happily and snatched the mocs up from the floor.

"Great to see you too. Gotta go." I waved to her and shot Steve a look. He nodded and even managed a slight smile. I hit the door almost running.

Of course, when I got to Phillip's, nobody was home. I waited a half-hour, listening to his songs and being sure not to nod off. I wasn't going to be taken by surprise again. But to no avail. It was Saturday and I guessed he had gone away for the weekend, maybe up to the San Carlos reservation. I returned the next day on Sunday, but again nobody showed up and after about forty-five minutes I left.

I returned to Phillip's a couple of days later and missed him again. I tried again in a couple of days and again no go. Out of desperation I started stopping by every day a couple of times. Then one Wednesday morning, when I didn't have classes, I drove up. The door was open. I got out and at the screen door I heard a voice from within.

"What was that?" I peered inside.

"*Handah*, that's an Apache welcome, come on in." Phillip's voice carried easily from inside the apartment.

"Great," I said grabbing the door handle.

Phillip put out his hand in a stop gesture, then turned it palm up. We stared at each other and then I shrugged.

"*Keiban?*" Phillip asked. I ran back to the car and came back with the nearly forgotten items. Phillip was laughing.

"Why are you laughing at me? I been carrying these things around for weeks," I complained.

"Gone to lots of trouble, have you?" he chuckled.

"Yeah, actually I have," I replied.

"*Shiye*, your troubles are just beginning." He smiled, "I promise you that."

"Thanks for the reassurance," I answered, handing him the mocs. "Shi—what?"

"*Shiye*, my son in *Ndee*—Apache language. Nope, not like that." He pushed the mocs back at me. "Here, take some of this." He handed me an Apache flat basket from the table piled with a fine, bright yellow powder—the same powder stains I had noticed on the moccasins.

"What is it?" I peered at the pile suspiciously.

"That's *haddentin*, cattail pollen. Like Catholic holy water. Take a pinch in your right hand."

I did as I was told. "Now with your thumb and forefinger, make a circle on my right instep."

"What am I doing?" I asked in exasperation, as I bent down to put the pollen on his foot. This was bordering on crazy. Here I was in an old Apache medicine man's house who barely spoke to me, and after paying for his mocs, doing some weird ritual so he would accept them.

"Never talk in ceremony. Talk means thoughts, thoughts equal ego, ego brings closure, and closure means disconnection from *Ulsen.*

"*Ulsen?*" I looked up.

"The One God."

"What, as opposed to the many gods?"

"Yes, exactly."

I started work again and he stopped me.

"Clockwise, always with the sun," he said. I resumed tracing clockwise.

"Now make a cross, first a horizontal line west to east." I hesitated confused.

"From your left to right," his voice was calm and slow and I could tell he was coaching me.

"Now south to north." I did so.

"Go to put the *keiban* on my foot four times." Tired of bending over, I knelt down.

"*Enju,*" he said when I looked at him. He was smiling and it made me feel good and warm inside—like a little kid who had been complimented about his toys by an adult.

"I don't understand," I complained.

"Start to lay the *keiban* on my foot three times." Phillip bent down and gently took one side of the moccasins. But instead of pulling them towards him, he pushed them back towards me, then back towards him, then me, then him, then me, then him, four times. On the fourth time he took the keiban.

"Feels pretty good, huh?" he asked.

"What?"

"Droppin' ego, openin' up, letting go. That is what it means to be an Apache, to become a humble two-leg standing straight on *Shima,* the earth mother, reaching to *Shitaa,* the sky father. And we the *Ndee,* the living humans, are in the balance between." He smiled wider.

"Yeah, I guess it does," I admitted. I did feel good and inexplicably warm.

"What are we doing?" I sat down cross-legged on the floor and he sat back down on the cheap kitchen chair. I felt like a grandkid at the feet of a grandparent, but strangely it didn't bother me at all—it felt quite natural, as if that is exactly where I should be at that moment. "You said ceremony. I mean what ceremony?"

"You are slow, as well as late. The gifting ceremony you just did."

"Gifting ceremony for what?" I was once again totally confused.

"For your training. We are recognizing and commemorating the luminous connection established between us through this physical ceremony. Don't you feel different?"

"I do," I said. I did, as a matter of fact.

"Feel this?" Phillip took his right hand from his solar plexus and slowly extended it out towards my abdomen. Although I was sitting several feet away on the floor, I immediately felt an even greater sensation of warmth and well being physically wash over me, but from the inside out. It was calming, reassuring and very comforting. I tingled and it tickled. It felt so good I laughed out loud.

"What was that?" I looked up at him in amazement.

"That," he said slowly, looking at me intently, "is what you are here to learn."

"Droppin' ego, openin' up, letting go."

I did not realize it at the time, but most of the world's problems are caused by a failure to drop one's ego, open up and let go.

It's that simple. But not that easy.

Try inhaling deeply through your nose, pause, and exhale deeply via your mouth.

Repeat until whatever emotion gripping you fades.

Open up to the possibility of a new point of view, a fresh interaction or a different relationship.

If you open up to a new dynamic, it's best if you let go of the past.

It's impossible to move forward if you keep going backward.

Sounds simple, but it's not.

The majority of people are too undisciplined to drop ego.

Too afraid to open up.

And terrified of letting go.

But if you can drop ego, open up and let go, the world is your oyster.

It also really helps when you have kids.

PURIFICATION

Whites fear death. Every time someone dies,
they act like it is a surprise, as if it wasn't going to happen.
So they instinctively think it's all over.
That's because they believe in soul and spirit
but they have never seen it. Indian people fear the dead,
because they can see ghosts, and the spirit world.
Indians believe to see. Non-Indians must see to believe.
—JRP

"LET'S GO FOR A RIDE." Phillip walked over to the passenger side door of my car. I followed him and got in the driver's side. He squeezed his long frame into the tiny passenger seat, his knees up to his chin. I got into the driver's seat and looked back over at him. The tall Apache elder looked absurd in my tiny Italian sports car.

"What?" Phillip stared gravely back.

"It's just that you look... ridiculous." I broke out laughing. I just could not help myself any longer. Phillip looked at me for a long moment. Then he too started to laugh.

"Let's go," he said.

I started her up and Phillip's singing came blaring through the speaker. Now it was my turn to be embarrassed. Phillip started laughing again and shook his finger.

"Proves my point exactly. There's just no getting around it," he laughed. "Too bad for you, though."

"Huh?" I said. I was spending a lot of time being confused around Phillip.

"Practicing singing already, aren't you?" It was barely a question.

"Maybe, a little," I admitted. "So?" I felt my face turning red.

"Before you can be a singer, you must be a warrior. And before you can become a warrior, you must first become a man. First catch the horse, and then fit the saddle." He leaned forward and turned off his songs. "That will be hard enough. But don't worry. You're in the right place even if you are slow and late."

"Right," I said, suppressing an urge to do a Bill Cosby and ask, "What's a singer?" I was getting used to Phillip's one-liners. I decided to just store the ones away that I did not understand at the time, which for now meant, well, all of them. "Well, I'll stop being slow right now. Where to?"

"West up Speedway—out to Gate's Pass." He pointed out in the general direction. I turned right onto Speedway obediently and hit the gas. It was late afternoon and the sun was low on the horizon and shining right into my eyes.

"I can hardly see anything, the sun's shining right in my eyes," I complained. I took one hand off the wheel and flipped down my visor. That didn't help much so I put my right hand out in front of me to block the sun directly. That worked a little better.

"How about that," Phillip mused.

I picked up speed and headed up into the saguaro-studded foothills. I had to switch hands though because I couldn't shift gears with my left. But when I shifted with my right, I was blind again. Plus I had to swerve frequently to stay on the steep-sided, curving road up into the mountains. We passed a sign that read "Sahuaro National Monument."

"I'm just about driving blind here," I warned.

"The old ones called that *Shekinah*," Phillip said.

"Shekihuh?" I thought I was pretty funny. I looked over at Phillip. He was still dead serious.

"*Shekinah*. The light from the heavens that blinds the eyes to illuminate the soul."

"Old ones—who's that, the Anazazi?" I asked while overcompensating on a stiff turn. My tires squealed. A Mustang driver coming the other direction sounded his horn angrily at me for crossing the center line.

"No, the Israelites. Slow down there, cowboy. The first rule is to show up. The second is to show up alive." Phillip started fussing with his seat.

"What are you looking for?" I asked.

"My seat belt, what else?" He did not even look up. After a moment I heard a click.

"Now where was I?" Phillip asked.

"Jews, old ones and *shekinah,*" I said helpfully. I put two hands on the wheel to negotiate a difficult curve.

"Israelites, not Jews. The Israelites, like Indians, were tribal people. The Jews are the descendants of the tribes."

"What's the point, why the distinction?" I asked.

"Got a girl friend?" Phillip changed the subject.

"Well, I had one in Ohio named Jenny. But I just met a great girl at the U of A named Ruth, great legs, great—"

"Okay, okay, Romeo, I get the idea. Thinking about marryin' one of 'em?" Phillip waved his hand in the air to clear the testosterone.

"No way, I'm a college student," I protested. "I—"

"Got it, okay. But if you were—just play along here, how could you tell what kind of woman she'd be in later years?" He was talking to me slowly again and I could tell he was coaching me.

"I don't know how," I shrugged, two hands on the wheel and squinting into the sun.

"You look at her mother. See what she's like: kind or sharptongued, a helpmate or a nag, fat or skinny, get the idea?" He looked over at me.

"Got it." I almost said "chief" but was pretty sure that would not go over well. "So I look at the mom to see what the daughter will end up like."

"Exactly. And if you want an even clearer picture, whom else?"

"The grandmother?"

"Right, and if there is still a *shiwoye hosteen*, a great grandmother—even better."

"Because then I can see the similarities and the differences of several generations." Finally I was tracking.

"And wouldn't that give you a better idea about what kind of wife she would be and more importantly what kind of daughter you might have. And what kind of granddaughter?"

"Sure, that makes sense."

"That is why the lineage of a people like the Jews or the *Ndee*—Apache—is so important."

"Uh, why again?" I asked regretfully, knowing that I was once again missing the point. Phillip shook his head and grinned.

"Every two-legged, four-legged, or winged is born, lives, eats, mates, births and dies. Does each species on earth do the same thing in the same way?"

"Of course not."

"The sparrow eats the grass seed. The bird lives, fights, mates and eventually dies and falls and finally returns to and becomes part of mother earth. Then maybe that seed was still in the sparrow's stomach, or another bird shits out a seed into that bird earth, and presto—grass grows. It's a great web of life—of hoops within hoops within hoops—just like a hoop dancer."

"Yeah, I saw those guys at a powwow in Tucson. Amazing how they connected all those hoops all over their bodies while in constant motion." I was glad I was doing something right for a change. "Pretty cool."

"Pretty cool…yes, well, those hoop dancers are the social and sport version of the *Ndee* curing ceremony—where the *diyin* and the *gan* pass hoops over the patient—like an old time MRI—but for the soul. Understand?" He looked over at me expectantly.

After a long moment, I nodded. "I understand the concept but that's just symbolic, isn't it? I mean it doesn't really *mean* anything, does it? And what's a *Diyin* and *Ga'an*?"

"We'll get to those later. Not just yet, but soon. Pull in here." He pointed off to the right side of the road.

I turned off into the Gates Pass Park pull-off and stopped. There were a few cars and trucks with tourists, hikers and scattering of local kids picnicking and waiting for the sunset—which promised as always to be gorgeous.

"Come on, let's go." For an old guy, he hopped out of my little car with surprising alacrity and headed away from the picnic area and straight up the mountain.

"Where are we going?" I asked, hurrying to keep up.

Phillip pointed with his lips, indicating the top of the mountain. "So, just as you can see what your woman will be like by looking back at her mother and grandmother, you can see what a people will be like by looking at their ancestors. Then you can see what their descendants will be like as well. And why is that important?"

"I give up," I replied after a couple of steps. "Why?"

"Because a people, like a person, can have a destiny, an important duty that must be fulfilled."

"Such as?"

"Now that is a good question," he replied.

As we walked, I looked out at the view. I hadn't really been able to appreciate it on the drive up. I had been too busy trying to keep on the road and not going blind. But now the Arizona-Sonora desert stretched out before us at sunset in all of its timeless, sharp-edged splendor. The horizon glowed gold, orange and red, and the rocky landscape reflected a molten yellow. As every sunset in Tucson, it was extraordinary.

Phillip looked at me while we walked uphill. He wasn't even breathing hard, even though he had been talking non-stop, while I was already huffing and puffing—and had barely said a word. I shrugged. I did not have a clue again.

"Like the winged, every species of sparrow has a way of life and a mission and a destiny, a purpose in its hoop on the web. And what did *Nayaez'kanee* say about sparrows?"

"Who?"

"The translation from the Apache is Slayer of Dragons."

"Who?" I asked.

"They called him *Yeshua Ben Yoseph.*" He looked at me. I stared back blankly. "In English—Jesus."

"Oh. I know this one—not a sparrow falls that your heavenly father does not see it." Phillip smiled. "So you mean that Jesus existed in the Apache tradition?"

"Warriors and healers are the basis of all traditions." He slapped me on the back. I stumbled on a rock and caught myself on an ocotillo.

I stopped and looked down the steep cliff face. We had climbed quite a way and the sheer drop was well over a hundred feet to rocky bottom. Later I learned that every year a couple of hapless tourists fell to their deaths, unprepared for the rugged terrain and the lack of any banisters or railings. This was still very much the Wild West.

"Ow, damn!" I looked at my hand. It was bleeding freely from the punctures caused by the sharp spines of the long, whip-like ocotillo branch. Phillip smiled.

"What?"

"Cussin' a cactus because it has spines is like cursing the desert because it doesn't have enough water. Silly. The utility of the cactus is its spines. The desert is the desert because it is dry. Its utility is that it is a dry and hard place to live and it makes the peoples that choose it, Jews, Muslims, and Apaches, hard, lean and clean. And when you de-emphasize the physical, you can access the spiritual. When you go up high like we are, it is easier to access the spiritual." He looked at me, "Let's go," and took off. I followed.

"The people of the word all came out of the desert," he muttered.

I looked at him, "What word?"

"The book," he said.

"What book?"

"The Word, the Book. Jews, Christians, Muslims. Same seed Word. Same Book. Same desert. Same mountains."

We had reached the top. There was no higher point to go to. Far below us was the parking area, and behind Speedway snaked back to Tucson. A forest of giant, many-armed saguaros surrounded us—the wind whistling eerily through their spines.

On the other side of the pass the cliff dropped straight off now hundreds of feet. I could not even see the bottom. The desert opened up before us vast, wild and unending. We could see for hundreds of miles. Old Tucson, the movie set, was visible in the distance.

Beyond that I could even make out the world famous Arizona-Sonora Desert Museum—actually a living zoo, and beyond that the ocean of desert, limitless, vast and fading into the infinity of the horizon of the earth itself. You could not look out there and not feel humbled by the grandness of the land itself. It was unforgettable.

"This is our desert. Our mountains" The anthros say—"

"Anthros?" I asked.

"Anthropologists. Don't interrupt. The anthros say the Apache came down here from the far north. Say our *keiban* were like *Innuit mukluks*, and our language roots prove it."

He turned away and looked out at the vast panorama before him. The setting sun cast him in gold and the wind blew through his hair and clothes. His profile showed the classic hawk features of the Apache. In a set of traditional Apache clothes he could have stepped right out of an old Western. He stared out there for a long time and then finally turned back to me. His eyes were narrow slits against the sun and wind.

"But we were here before the rocks were hard."

"You said it's easier to access the spiritual at heights. But what is spiritual?" I asked. The wind whipped at me.

"That which is not physical."

"Is that why we are way up here?" I was starting to tingle all over again. Maybe it was just the cold from the wind and the setting sun.

"Every people has a purpose, a destiny, a mission and a duty. Long ago in the before time, before history, before man—"

"Before man," I interrupted again, "when was that?"

"Before man was the *Adamas*. And what does Adam mean?" He looked hopefully at me. I stared back.

"People of the red earth made from blood and clay." He was deadly serious now, and stared intensely at me. "And what do you feel *Chihinne-Nde'e* means?"

My mind was blank. Then, "Red clay people," popped out of my mouth. I somehow knew it. The tingling intensified.

"*Ow*, yes that's right. From old desert to new desert. Old mountain to new mountain. Israelites all the way to Apache. The sons of the Addamics are the human beings, that went off in the four directions from the Eden kept garden place between the rivers—where Iraq is now—they went off in the four directions on their quests and in doing so became the four peoples, black, red, yellow and white. They formed the four roads of human civilization, and the ages of humanity for childhood, youth, adulthood and old age—and the seasons of life for spring, summer, fall and winter. Each forms an integral part of the hoop, each maintained the survival of mankind in their time and place of crisis and war."

I had never heard him talk so much at once and I struggled to absorb it all. His eyes were bright beyond the sunlight and fixed me in place. A current flowed through me and I shook.

"Which brings us to you."

"Me. What does this all have to do with me?" I looked back out at the vast desert plain. Phillip rolled his eyes and sighed expansively.

"I just told you—never mind, no more time for talk. The sun is setting. Sit down over there but straight; tuck your left leg under your thigh. See, if you were wearing *keiban,* you'd be sitting on buckskin, not rock or cacti."

"Yeah, but I'm not and this rock hurts."

"Stop whining like a boy. Start acting like a man." Phillip's tone slapped my ego down hard which, I learned much later, was his precise intention.

"Tuck your chin like a cadet brace; put your tongue on the roof of your mouth. Stop thinking. Watch yourself breathe. Watch the breath go in and out of you—like a swinging door."

"But what am I doing?" I even sounded whiny to me.

"You came to learn, didn't you?" Phillip's voice was like flint. There was the first hint of anger in it that I had ever heard, and I decided I did not want to hear any more.

"I'm here to learn," I admitted.

"Then shut up, sit up and pay attention," he snapped. I did as I was told.

Phillip took a deep breath. "Now just relax. Watch your breathing. In through your nose, pause, and out through the mouth, pause, then repeat the cycle." His tone retuned to its normal calm monotone.

I sat up straight. I tucked my chin and put my tongue on the roof of my mouth. Something electric shuddered up from my groin along my spine and up to the crown of my head.

"We are not people of the word, nor the book. Our way is different. We too are a covenant people. But of an even older way, older than the *Adama* and the Eve." Phillip's voice was calm and soothing.

I began to watch my breathing.

"That's better. Now, did you eat today?"

"No, I left before breakfast."

"So you fasted since breakfast. *Enju*—good. And aren't you thirsty?"

"I am, yes," I hadn't noticed, but I was. I couldn't remember the last time I had taken a drink.

"And the climb up here," Phillip intoned, "it tired you, yes?"

"Yes, sir."

"And you are at an altitude higher than you are used to, aren't you?—the air is thinner."

"It is."

"So the physical is definitely weakened, right?"

"Right." What physical, I thought to myself. Pretty funny. Phillip's voice was becoming even more soothing and more distant. My world was only my chest breathing in and then out and then pausing."

"Starting at the top of your head, with each exhalation, let go of any tension in your head, ears, eyebrows, even your eyes—that means your eyelids will go three-quarters closed, and your eyes will unfocus." I relaxed my scalp, my head, even my eyes, and my vision did blur.

"Now let go of any tension in your mouth, jaw, neck, upper torso and back." I relaxed even more. My tongue dropped from the top of my mouth. My lips drooped open; as the moments ticked by, I even began to drool.

"With the next exhalation relax your abdominals—only leave those lower back muscles tense needed to keep you upright." Phillip's voice was far away and faint. I was weak and tired.

"…any tension in the toes and soles of your feet." I must have drifted off, but it was easy now to continue to let go.

"Watch your breath slow even more."

The wind whipped against my body, but I no longer felt the outside of me. I was deep inside myself. I watched through soft, blurred vision an ant crawl on my forearm. But I didn't feel it. My breathing was slow, deep and measured.

"Now watch your heartbeat slow. Don't try to make it slow; just watch it happen. Count the number of beats per breath cycle—for example, inhalation, then simply watch it slow. Probably from five or six, to three or four."

I was deep inside myself now and Phillip was almost gone. I could barely hear him. I could only watch my breathing. I counted five beats per inhalation. Two cycles later I counted only four, then a couple more—only three.

"If a thought comes, let it go, and return to watching your breathing."

Phillip stopped talking for a long while. I could hear the wind whistling through the saguaros. Somewhere in the distance a hawk screamed....

"And when you are ready, leaving your eyes unfocused, using soft, unfocused peripheral vision, open your eyes."

Slowly, reluctantly and with great difficulty, I struggled to open my heavy, unresponsive eyelids. Finally I succeeded. Phillip was a dark outline standing in front of me about twenty feet away, at the edge of the cliff. Behind him the sun was a huge gold, fiery ball, bright against the red, blue and green of the evening sky.

"...look past my head and shoulders into the distance of the sky and only with soft, peripheral vision, view my head and shoulders. And now... it is time to—*see!*"

Phillip was silhouetted against the giant ball of the sun, which was dropping rapidly behind him. I was struck by the primordial beauty and power of the place and the moment. Then the glowing gold orb of the fireball sun was disappearing along the distant curve of the earth itself. I don't recall the precise moment, because I was not looking at anything in particular, that is, my vision was still unfocussed—when suddenly, without warning—the luminous world snapped into focus.

Phillip's darkened form was silhouetted against the sunset sky. But now all around him was a thin, sharply defined electric outline of brilliant, bluish-white light! At first I wondered where Phillip had gotten the neon light from and how he had rigged it so quickly and tightly around his body.

Then I saw the band of light pulse and brighten in places, flaring and fading slightly with a pulse all its own, as if from the beat of his very soul. The luminescence was transparent and I could see the final rays of the setting sun through it.

Sparkles of light, like tumbling snowflakes, raced around the edges of the glow and even drifted up and out of it like tiny self-luminous bubbles, drifting up instead of down, and out into the darkening sky until they blended seamlessly with the emerging night stars.

I suddenly and abruptly inhaled—finally remembering to breathe after a long, painful moment. My chest stretched and heaved painfully as I drank in another, deep full breath. I shuddered and then collapsed forward with the effort of my intensity. I don't know how long I lay there, but it was for a long time. Finally, I put one hand out in front of me and lifted myself up with great effort.

"For those with eyes to see," I murmured. Phillip squatted down in front of me.

"Amen." He was smiling again.

"Stop whining like a boy. Start acting like a man."

Fold a blanket into a square, then a triangle. Sit with your butt on the blanket and your legs off. Sit up straight.

Sit across from a partner.

Tuck your left leg under your thigh into man seat.

Tuck your chin. Put your tongue on the roof of your mouth. Stop thinking.

To stop thought, just watch yourself breathe. Watch the breath go in and out of you—like a swinging door.

Relax. Watch your breathing. In through your nose, pause, and out through the mouth, pause, then repeat the cycle.

Starting at the top of your head, with each exhalation, let go of any tension in your head, ears, eyebrows, even your eyes—that means your eyelids will go three-quarters closed, and your eyes will unfocus.

Now let go of any tension in your mouth, jaw, neck, upper torso and back.

With the next exhalation relax your abdominals—only leave those lower back muscles tense needed to keep you upright.

Let go of any tension in your upper legs, then lower legs.

Release control of your toes and soles of your feet.

Watch your breath slow.

Now watch your heartbeat slow

Count the heartbeats per inhalation. As your heartbeat slows, the number will drop.

If a thought comes, let it go, and return to watching your breathing.

When ready, leaving your eyes unfocused, using soft, unfocused peripheral vision, open your eyes.

Look past your partner's head and shoulders.

And for the first time in your life—truly see!

Pretty wild huh?

NO MAN TELLS
ANOTHER WHAT TO DO

When I was a child, I used to speak like a child,
think like a child, reason like a child; when I became a man,
I did away with childish things.
—Corinthians 13:11

I DON'T REMEMBER how we hobbled down that mountain in the gathering darkness. But we did. We eventually found my car and got moving. For a long time we were silent. Finally I broke the silence.

"Are you going to tell me what that was?" I asked.

"Nope," Phillip replied.

"Why not?" I looked over briefly at Phillip. He was looking straight ahead, arms crossed, as if he was about to nod off. Then I returned my attention to the road. It was dark now and the windy road down the mountain was easy to over-drive and go right over a steep cliff.

"I am not going to tell you anything."

"Huh?" I chanced a look back. His head was down.

"No man tells another what to do. That is freedom and manhood. A man has to figure things out for himself," he said. "That's enough for today, anyway." He went silent.

I drove him home. I reached over to nudge him awake, but he sat up just before I touched him. He stepped out of the car and shut the door. I was about to put it in gear when he leaned down on the door. The window was open.

"Now would be a real good time to quit."

He stood up and walked to his door, unlocked it, and went inside without ever looking back. I sat there with my engine idling for a while trying to decipher his closing message. Phillip had not said it with any menace. It wasn't a threat. And he had been expecting me for a long time. He had opined that last remark with his slightly sad, wry hint of a smile. I looked back at the house. The windows remained dark. Finally I left.

I could not wait to get back to Phillip's, but class was in session and I was busy for the first part of the week. But while in history class I experienced an amazing revelation.

On Monday morning I was slouching in a lecture chair watching the professor drone on when something extraordinary happened. As I relaxed my focus of vision, a tight, bright, neon halo snapped into sharp focus around the prof's head and shoulders. The clarity of it startled me and I bolted forward in my seat—enough to disturb the lecture.

"Is there a problem, young sir, or did we just wake you?" The teacher was on his game and the class laughed it up.

"Sorry, sir." I crossed my arms, legs, shook my head and slumped back down in embarrassment.

After a moment, I sat up straighter. Then I remembered Phillip's coaching at the Pass. I sat up even straighter, tucked my chin and slowed my breathing. Once I had my breathing reduced, I focused on slowing my heart. This took longer, but after a while I could definitely count fewer beats per breath cycle. My heart had slowed. I relaxed my vision once more into a peripheral seeing only. Instantly the halo popped back around the teacher. But this time it was around his entire body. It was a translucent white, thick for a couple of inches off his frame until it abruptly disappeared, and as I saw, I realized it was pulsing!

Things got even wilder then. I learned not to focus on the light, but only *see* at it indirectly with soft vision—to see the space around the person. Suddenly halos popped around all the student heads sitting in front of me! Everybody had one. It was mind boggling.

I slowly looked left and continued to see luminous lights around the student heads there. I turned right and saw glowing heads as well. Everywhere everyone glowed with the body electric. It was if someone had just turned on the lights on the human race. Involuntarily I laughed out loud in sheer delight. Literally in the blink of an eye, the room and my world had changed forever.

In unison the entire auditorium turned to look at me. I was ready this time though and kept my eyelids half-closed, and my vision blurry. The professor walked my way too. But as the class turned, so did their luminous halos.

As the teacher walked over with a stern look on his glowing face, so did his electric outline. I laughed even more. By the time the professor crossed the lecture floor, I was nearly helpless with laughter. My laughter was contagious and pretty soon the whole lecture hall was guffawing with me. But just as the professor reached my desk, I was literally saved by the bell. (I nearly failed that class.)

I couldn't wait to tell Phillip. I cut class and headed over to his place. Of course he wasn't there. I came back later that afternoon but again no Phillip. I stopped by Steve's—nobody home there either. I even came back after dinner, but Phillip had once again just disappeared.

By the next morning I was desperate to see Phillip. I stopped by his place around 8 AM. There he was—sitting at his battered old kitchen table reading the paper and drinking coffee.

"*Handah,*" he called to me as I peered through the screen door, "Been waitin' for you. Come on in." I did.

"I can't believe it. I've been seeing halos on everybody—it's amazing! Everyone has this light around them—not just you." I was going on and on.

"Whoa, slow down there, cowboy," Phillip was chuckling. He put up his hand.

"What?" I asked, truly puzzled.

"So I guess this means you've decided not to quit?" Now Phillip looked serious.

"Of course not. Why would I want to do that?" I was serious too—and confused.

Phillip rubbed his chin slowly. "Sit down." He indicated the chair across from him. "Coffee?"

"Please," I replied. He got up, poured me a cup and refilled his, then sat back down. I took a sip. It was, I would learn later, Indian coffee—sweet, black and steaming hot.

"I was serious when I asked you to consider quitting."

"I don't understand why I would quit."

"By the time you do, it will be too late," he replied.

"I don't get it. I thought you said you've been waiting for me—that I am, like late." I blew on my coffee. "And what about that whole ceremony thing?"

"True enough," he said, "But I don't want to waste my time or yours."

"Fair enough. What kind of time are we talking about?"

"Now."

"I don't get it. What does now mean?"

"Now means now. It means that it has taken your and my entire lifetimes to bring us together for this time—now."

"Sounds important."

Phillip looked directly at me. "I have dedicated my life to preserving the *Ndee* way. That is what I was called upon to do by *Ulsen.* I have been successful in my calling. I have helped to restore that which we Apache lost in the wars and after as a conquered people. I have helped to restore our most sacred ceremonies of wisdom and power that were outlawed when our parents and grandparents were banished to Florida and Alabama and Oklahoma." He paused to sip his coffee.

"Now," he pointed at me with his chin, "I am called to teach you."

"Why—am I supposed to help preserve Apache culture?" I asked.

"I don't know what your destiny is. That is your problem to figure out. I just know that my destiny is to train you—if you are willing to learn. Are you?"

"Yes. I am." I said it firmly. "When do we start?"

"We already have."

"So what now?"

"You were telling me that you can now see, that you now have the sight."

"Yeah—it's amazing, incredible!"

"So what is it that you see?" He had me there. I was so excited by seeing that I hadn't yet thought about what I was seeing.

"Is it physical, that light?" He was coaching me again.

"No, it's not physical, but it is there. I wasn't seeing...." My voice trailed off.

"The spaces around the people?" He smiled.

"Yes. That's it," I replied excitedly.

"There is more than one way to see. When you hunt, you don't look at each tree on the mountain to see which the deer is taking shade under, because there are too many. Instead you see the entire mountainside and let your eye be drawn to the deer's movement or form. Indian people see far. Non-Indians see close to read individual letters on pages of books. Custer's Crow scouts could see the Cheyenne and Lakota camp with their bare eyes when Custer could not even with his binoculars. Apache medicine men and women—our seers—could see the enemy far away, in distance and even in time. Anyway, if what you see is not physical, then is it spiritual?"

"Yes, it must be," I admitted.

"Ever seen it before?" He turned and looked with obvious formality at a print on the wall. I looked too and saw an Indian Madonna and child scene. Around the baby Jesus and Mary were, of course, halos.

"Yes, sir, of course, it's in every picture of Jesus and Mary and the saints ever done."

"That's right. Because a long time ago, somebody was watching Jesus intently until they saw, then they drew it down. But later on, others did not see; they just looked at the painting, and they said, well, it must just be symbolic—a symbolic representation of holiness."

"But it is real."

"It is real and it is, by your own admission, spiritual—so are you seeing spiritual energy and power?"

"Yes, I guess I am."

"And to whom does it belong and where is it originating from, this now visible spiritual energy?"

"From you, from everybody—I mean everybody seems to have it. I've been seeing people everywhere in class, on campus, even in cars at a stoplight—everybody has it."

"And have you also noticed how, when you look into the car next to you, after a moment that person will look back?"

"Yes, sir, that's true, I did."

"So there must be some kind of non-physical connection alerting them, right?"

"Right."

"And now you have seen it. Have you seen those bumper stickers that say, 'Who Dies with the Most Toys Wins'?" I nodded, not wanting to interrupt since I finally had got him talking.

"White, modern, first world, industrial society believes in things, money and possessions—but not in spirits, soul, ghosts and the spirit world. They only believe in what they can see, and 'course they don't know how to see. They are like clever children, or half-asleep folk. Their physical skills—light bulbs, penicillin, bridges, buildings, roads—are amazing, but they know next to nothing about the spiritual, non-physical world. But if it is all about the physical and there is nothing more than that—then why not just die with the most toys, why not pimp women and sell drugs?" He stared at me.

"Because we are not just physical—we are spiritual as well." I shivered in the realization.

"Look around this room." For the first time I did. It was almost as filled as Steve's store. There were book shelves filled with heavy volumes. I saw a whole series by Thomas Mails, the famous Indian ethnographer. But everywhere there were ancient, Apache weapons, baskets and a number of beautiful buckskin contraptions I did not even recognize.

"No toys here, but a few manhood tools and warrior weapons."

He got up and went to a cluttered corner. He reached four times for it and then picked up a long seven-foot curved lance covered in fur. On the top end it curved like a shepherd's crook. Four huge, white, black-tipped feathers dangled from a dark cord that ran from the tip of the curve across to the main shaft. The whole thing was covered in luxurious brown fur. He stood with it in his right hand and it seemed to somehow become a part of him.

"The feathers are *itsa'a*—eagle for the four directions and dimensions of *diyi*. Look," he said and peeled back the hide. "The hide is beaver because it builds a lodge over the waters like *Izlandelahe.*"

"Is—" I looked at him lost again. His look was stern and so I shut up.

"It's tied here with deer sinew to include the power of the forest four-legged also. Now look here under at the yucca staff." He peeled back a portion of the hide near the bottom tip. It was an old faded red. "Why red?"

"Red clay—*Adama?*" I shrugged.

"Yes, but there is always more to see and know. Look here now." He peeled back a center area of the shaft, which was a mild yellow.

"Seen that before?"

"Yes, sir, it kind of looks like the color of the ... the luminosity I saw around you."

"Good, right, now look here." He peeled back the hide at the top of the shaft. It was a faded but deep purple.

"Purple." I blurted out.

"Or?"

"Or what?"

"Another term for purple," he sighed, and I hoped he would call me slow again as my mind raced. "Look, red at the bottom, yellow in the middle, violet at the top."

"It's a spectrum! Infrared to visible yellow to violet to ultraviolet. It's a tool for seeing!"

"*Enju shiye'e, enju.*" He returned the lance to the corner, extending it four times before hanging it back on a nail on the fourth.

"I've never seen Apaches use those curved coup sticks in any of my books."

"Yeah, sometimes we forget to follow the anthro's scripts. But the point is that you now know there is a spiritual world. How," he asked slowly, "do you know?"

"I know," I said slowly, "because I have seen the spirit." Phillip slowly turned around. The lance was directly behind him, heading upwards behind his head. He clapped his hands together once in a strange solo applause, then pointed at me.

"The boy that you were born has begun to die. The man you must become is beginning to be trained."

**"The boy that you were born has begun to die.
The man you must become is beginning to be trained."**

Sit up straight on your folded blanket in man seat, chin tucked. Have your partner stand in front of you.

If you are in class as I was, a professor on a podium works great too.

Start a good breath cycle.

When your breathing slows, slow your heart.

After your heartbeat slows, just watch your breathing.

With your peripheral vision pick up the luminous glow about the head and shoulders of the prof or your partner.

As they walk slowly side to side, trail their movement with soft, unfocused sight.

When they stand still, see what else floats about them.

Guess it's really not about the toys, is it?

THE BODY ELECTRIC

We are defined by our duties—
and how impeccably we execute these duties, to others.

—JRP

"How so?" I was confused again. Phillip leaned forward across the table. His eyes glittered.

"Because you have just learned that there is something beyond the physical—something spiritual, something worth killing for, something worth dying for, something worth living for."

"And that means...." My voice trailed off.

"There are things worth sacrificing for, things beyond yourself, beyond this life, this world—this veil."

"Manhood begins here and now. A man or woman in an Apache family, band, tribe even nation, is defined by their duties to others. Nothing is possible in a tribe on your own. When we hunted, we hunted together like mountain lions, one hunter herding the prey, the other making the kill. Our women could not put up a tepee alone. One had to stand on the shoulders of the other. None of our ceremonies can be performed alone, nor even afforded alone." He sipped his coffee.

"Our most sacred ceremony is the *Na'iies,* which means 'now it happens'."

"Now what happens?"

"When a maiden has her first moon."

"Moon?"

"Her first blood, her first menstruation. But in American it is called the Changing Ceremony or the Sunrise Way."

I pondered his answer for a moment. "We don't have anything like that nowadays do we?"

"Not really. *Bar Mitzvahs* and *Quincineras*. But they are really just symbolic. They no longer contain *diyi*—*Ulsen's* power. But we will get to that later, if you hang on. The point is I have spent most of my life restoring the Sun Rise to our people. But we are poor since we now count our value in the American way of money and personal possessions. So even though a ceremony costs a family maybe ten, fifteen thousand dollars—no one family can afford that."

"So what do they do—take out a loan?" I asked.

"Exactly—but it is an Apache loan. The collateral is human. A loan of *shita'kee.*"

"Shit—" I just couldn't resist. I was after all a college student. I smiled. So did he.

"*Shita'kee*, it means 'what's mine is yours.' Indians share as a people. If one is hungry, everyone is hungry. If one has money, everybody has some. We are the only true socialists, though we are way too patriotic to ever call ourselves such. For the feast we go to a cousin—and say cousin, and call them to their face by their Apache name, so that they know this is important, and we ask for a steer for the thanksgiving meal. Then we go to another relative for the groceries, and so on. But in a couple of years, those cousins, will come back and ask for a steer or groceries for their daughter's Sun Rise. That," he said, "is *shita'kee.*"

"So everyone is financially indebted to each other all the time?" I frowned.

"Everyone is indebted, but financially is only one aspect, and the least important part of the debt. The important thing is that they are all connected by interwoven obligations year after year, ceremony after ceremony, and generation after generation."

"I'm sorry, I'm not sure I get your point."

Phillip shook his head and smiled. He looked upwards. "This is the one? After all my work?" He looked back at me kindly but a little sadly. He rubbed his chin thoughtfully, then began again. "Indians address each other by their duty names."

"Like once I saw an Indian mom with her kids in the airport, and she kept calling to them saying, 'Come, my children.' Is that what you mean?" I interjected. Phillip nodded.

"Yes, she identified them to everyone, claiming them as 'my children.' That's why we say *Dagote'e, shiyee*, 'how are you, my son,' or *shilgonte'e, shiwoye'e*, 'I'm well, grandfather.' We address each other formally by our duties to them and by their duties to us, to remind us of our *shita'ke*, of our obligations...."

"As adults," I said triumphantly, finally getting it, "as real men and women who are defined by their roles as mothers and fathers." Phillip clapped his hands together.

"Brothers and sisters. Sons and daughters. That's it. Now you are thinking like a real man. Now you get it." He was beaming and I was all warm inside again. His affect on me was amazing. His authenticity always touched me deeply. He generally wanted to help me and teach me.

"But also beyond our most essential roles as family members, to our other roles. That's why we still say Teacher—Doctor—Preacher. We don't use first names for these folks, because they are not just our friends; they are special and have special obligations to us which we always want to respect, and respectfully remind them of as well." He laughed. "Pretty good Apache cunning, huh?"

I laughed too. He was not the deadly, serious Apache medicine chief I had expected.

"You aren't exactly what I expected." I grinned. He nodded.

"I get that a lot." He crossed his arms, leaned back and stretched out his cowboy boots, then crossed them too.

"This is a new kind of *shita'kee*. I'm not defined any longer by Apache tradition alone. I am re-defining myself through new duties, for a new time—through you."

"Me again." I shook my head. "I don't get it; you mean I must re-define myself through my duties too?" Phillip nodded.

"But I don't even know my duties."

"Not yet. You are not even a true man yet—not in spirit, not yet—only in body."

"And that means I only know about collecting the toys?"

"Not at all. You are a good boy or you would not have gone to all the trouble you have to get here—and keep on returning. But you have yet to access the spiritual side of your manhood—so how can you expect to understand the duties thereof?"

Phillip turned the paper he had been reading around and slid it across the table to me. "Read the headlines. Read that." He tapped a headline.

"*Twelve Year Old Rapes and Kills Ten Year Old.* God, it seems like every day there's another terrible case like this." I shook my head sadly. "And each time they're even younger."

"Exactly. Do you ever remember things like this when you were growing up"?

"No, now that you mention it, I don't."

"Notice how rude and fat folks are now too."

"Yes, sir, I do."

"Why do you think these things are happening now?"

"Because … people are no longer defined by their duties—and they no longer prepare for their duties, so they aren't trained for their duties. But it's so obvious. We have no manhood training, no womanhood training today. So nobody is trained for adulthood."

"If it is so obvious, why ain't anybody doing anything about it?" Phillip asked rhetorically. "And how come it took you so long to show up and figure it out?"

"Because I'm slow as well as late," I admitted without ego or sarcasm. Surprisingly once again I felt better, cleaner, somehow lighter—maybe even taller.

"Right! That's better. Now you are starting to get it. No excuses. A free man is responsible for himself. And doesn't make excuses for his own choices. Adulthood is hard. I guarantee you one thing. If it hasn't got hard yet, it will *shiye*, it will."

"And since no one is trained, no one is prepared, and then these kids have kids and nobody has any clue what they are doing or what their duties are."

"When things get hard, and they always do, instead of defining themselves by their duties to others, they think only of themselves, and this," he tapped the headline again, "is the result."

He stood up. "More coffee? What happens to a civilization when it allows its children to be destroyed?"

I stood up as well and grabbed his cup. "I'll get it, grandfather." And I did. He sat back down.

"It kills itself off." I stopped and thought about that. "We're killing ourselves off."

"*Shiwoye'e*. In Apache grandfather is *shiwoye*." He said sipping the coffee. He nodded. "In the old days Ndee did not say thanks out loud. Not out of ingratitude but politeness. They figured if they had to say it, they were being too obvious and wanting you to consciously acknowledge their act or gift. They did not want to seem to be forcing anybody to do anything, so they did not say thanks out loud." He sipped again. "Today though we say *"Ahie'e."*

I smiled and remained quiet. I was starting to get the hang of this. It was a wholly different way of living, learning, communicating and interacting. And I liked it.

"Do you know who you are and what the term 'bastard' really means?" Phillip brought me out of my reverie. My stomach dropped a bit.

"I do. Because I am one. I come from Saint Joseph's orphanage in Cincinnati. I don't know my birth parents, but I know they weren't married. I know my genetic father never claimed me as his. And how the hell did you know that?" I was again confused but it sure seemed that Phillip had somehow known my personal history.

"We learn what we need to learn in the way we need to."

"What the hell does that mean?"

"It means that in *Ndee*, bastard is *yudasht'in*. And it means 'born outside.'"

"Born outside what."

"Outside of *bigowa*. It means house but signifies home. It means outside a clan, no family—and that means?" He looked at me without sympathy or judgment. This was about teaching.

"That means...no *shita'kee*, no burden, and no obligation."

"Yes." He leaned forward and lightly slapped my arm, "No *gowa*, no *shita'kee*, no *bigowa*—*no mi casa su casa*—my house is yours. The Mexicans, they stole that from us, you know. No connections."

He stood up and was suddenly taller than I had remembered. Perhaps it was the cowboy boots. He stepped into the other room for a moment and then returned with some rolled up blankets under his arm.

"Let's go outside." He walked out and the screen door slammed. I rose and followed him.

He had gone around the back of the low red-brick duplex to a small cottonwood grove and I hurried to catch up. He walked into the center of the grove. In it was a clearing. In the clearing was a domed lodge made of saplings with a pit to the left of a doorway in the front facing east. The sunlight dappled the sand in beautiful patterns that shifted with the rustling leaves. In the center a fire dwindled, just dying down and ringed with rocks to keep it from spreading. About thirty feet back was a small stream. A section had been damned with an old board and scooped out to form a small, shallow pool.

In the fire among the coals were more rocks, but these were porous and volcanic and glowing red with heat. They had obviously been in there since the fire had been started, probably hours before. Nearby was a pile of wood and a pile of blankets. Next to the lodge was a plastic water jug, a plastic water bucket, a pair of deer antlers, two drums—a small one and a larger one and some kind of bell and clacker. There was also an abalone shell, and improbably, a pitchfork.

"Had to bury those prairie dogs," Phillip said with a deadpan expression, and then walked into the trees. I didn't even slow down this time. I was getting the hang of Apache humor.

"This *tachin* is—"

"A sweat lodge," I chimed in.

He nodded. "This lodge is for our purification rite. It is a very old way of praying, of connecting to *Ulsen,* by weakening the physical to access the spiritual. Look at the construction."

I touched a sapling in the structure. But it was not one sapling but two. The sapling on the opposite side was woven around the near side one. Then I saw that the bark had been stripped off both saplings and had been used to tie the two together—the bark outer skin was turned inward I realized, to better grip the smooth surface of the sapling. Other saplings ran perpendicularly to this pair and were interwoven throughout the entire structure.

"It's so simple, it's ingenious!" I exclaimed. Phillip smiled.

"The old ways always are. Tap it with your hand." I did.

"It's strong." I was surprised.

"This one's maybe two years old. Setting out in the Arizona sun and rain, day after day, still strong."

"Wow. That long and still this strong." I was truly amazed.

"The strength," he said, fixing my gaze "is in the weave."

"Like *shita'kee,*" I said, finally following the trail Phillip was carefully laying out for me. Phillip was slowly nodding. He ran his brown hands over the yellow saplings.

"These willow, they bend and weave together. They form hoops within hoops. Here today, we begin a new *shita'kee,* you and me."

He ran his hand over the willow and reached out for mine. I extended it and he took it. "The American wars nearly destroyed us. But now Americans are destroying themselves. Our new *shita'kee* will help both our peoples."

"Yes," I said.

"You have seen the spiritual, now you need to learn to hear and smell it, even touch it too. Sit down in the lodge there."

I bent down. It was small. I barely fit through the doorway and I had to crawl to get inside.

"I can barely fit," I complained, as the cut end of a willow ripped my t-shirt.

"It fits you impeccably."

"How you figure that? I had to kneel to clear the door and crawl to get in!"

"Exactly. And you've got red earth all over you."

I looked at my palms and the knees of my jeans—all were covered in red dirt. I looked around at the ground. Running through the bottom of the lodge, under the normal buff colored dust of the Arizona desert floor, was a smear of reddish clay earth. There were four, old worn jute mats inside and I shifted onto one.

"Looks like Sedona," I said.

"Sedona is Apacheria." Phillip laid a blanket from the pile on the lodge.

"What?"

"Our land. Before those red rocks were hard, they were like this here." He spread another blanket over the lodge.

"So how did this little patch get here?"

"Rocks move. Earth moves. Same way we move, but on their time not ours. Some anyway. Those ones over in Death Valley, they race around there and leave a real good track. Drives those scientists nuts." He chuckled.

Once more I had no idea what he was talking about. But many years later I would be thumbing through a *National Geographic* and sure enough there were those prize-winning photos of several large, grapefruit and even basketball sized rocks with long furrows, and long since dried, fading into the flat, limitless horizon. This was just one of many times Phillip would teach me things that years later, I would come to understand—or at least learn were true.

Unaccountably Phillip began to casually disrobe. He unsnapped his Western shirt, pulled off his boots and socks and then his jeans. A small buckskin bag hung from his neck. A bunch of colored buckskin cords draped over his right shoulder and disappeared behind his left hip. He left on his boxers.

"What are you doing?" I asked finally.

"Better strip down too, if you're going to sweat with me." He tossed a blanket over the open top of the lodge. He adjusted the others quickly and in a moment I was in the dark. I sat for a moment.

The flap of the blanket over the door flipped back. Phillip stuck his head in, holding the abalone shell. The shell was filled with sand and on the sand were coals from the fire, still glowing red. He sprinkled something green on them which crackled and smoked, emitting a pleasant odor.

"Flat cedar to purify the lodge," he said. Then he whispered something else in Apache, and opened the bag around his neck. He reached inside and I could see the bright yellow of cattail pollen dusting his fingers. He sprinkled some in the pit, and then disappeared back outside.

I sat there for another moment not knowing quite what to do. I lifted the flap and saw that Phillip was now shoveling coals onto the pitchfork. He headed towards me and I helped open the flap.

He shoveled four red-hot lava rocks into the pit. The heat from the four rocks was startling and searing. I pulled off my t-shirt and struggled out of my jeans. Luckily I was wearing underwear that day. I kicked off my shoes. He sat down in the entrance.

"*Shi, shi okahi'i...*" he whispered. I lost the rest.

"Are you praying?" I asked. He gave me a withering look. I shut up.

He disappeared back outside. The rocks glowed in the dark. I began to sweat. In a moment he was back with more rocks. I don't know how many but a lot more than four. He disappeared outside again. I was sweating freely now and the interior was fairly well lit by the glowing rocks. Phillip appeared again with another load of rocks, and then was gone again. He returned with another load of rocks, and then repeated the ritual once more.

By the time he climbed inside the lodge, I was already sweating profusely, and he hadn't even poured any water on the rocks yet. He pulled the bucket full of water and the water jug inside with him.

He said something in Apache, then "East," and poured water on the rocks with the abalone shell. Living steam hissed dangerously and sprang upwards.

"Close your eyes when I pour," he said softly, almost reverently.

Again he uttered Apache and then "South." He intoned and poured again, and again steam exploded everywhere. The air was alive and hissing.

"West," he mumbled again in Apache. He poured again. The air was white hot. Phillip was a dim shape through the white haze.

More Apache, and then "North." He poured again and the rocks shrilled and crackled. The steam was so thick Phillip was gone. My heart pounded in my chest. I was soaked in sweat. I struggled to breathe. The heat was almost unbearable. My skin seemed to sizzle. By now I was listening closely.

"*Ni' gosdzan awolzanna*, when earth was made." The rocks hissed again, so he must have poured, but I could no longer tell, the steam was so thick. My vision closed. I was close to passing out.

"*Yaa awolzanna*—when sky was created." More steam, if that was possible. More heat. Unbelievable heat threatened to dissolve me then and there. My head swam. My whole body burned. I was afraid to open my eyes fearing that my eye balls would be seared.

The air was too hot to breathe in, so I covered my mouth. I blew out to cool the air between my palm and mouth with my breath. Hesitantly I inhaled slowly. I had to. I was out of breath. It burned a bit. I was dizzy and light-headed.

"Bend low. Put your head to the earth. It is cooler there." Phillip's voice wafted over to me sounding strangely muffled. I lowered my head and put my forehead on the ground. It was slightly less hot there and there was a slight thermocline just off the moist clay that was actually breathable.

"Drink." The plastic water jug appeared in the air. I took it, but the full weight of it dropped it to the floor. I was unbelievably weak. I slowly struggled to uncap the lid, then tilted it over. Cool water spilled onto my cheeks and into my mouth. I poured more on my head.

Then the rocks hissed as Phillip poured again. My forehead returned to the ground. The air was on fire. I scooped a shallow depression in the clay to try to breathe something cooler, but it didn't help.

The air hissed again. I squinted one eye slightly open. The little lodge was so fogged I could no longer see my own hands.

Time became immaterial and irrelevant as my world narrowed to simply trying to survive the crushing, unendurable heat of the lodge that permeated every pore of my body. The air hissed again, and again and again, until I lost count. I think Phillip was testing me. I wanted to tear my way out of there, but by now I was too weak. And I was determined not to quit. I began to fade in and out of consciousness. I felt the skin on my shoulders begin to blister.

"Drink," I heard him say, and I did, but in slow motion. I brought my head to the jug on the ground and then tilted it. The air hissed. I squeezed my eyes shut and hung on. I began to seriously pray to live through this.

I was barely conscious and time had long since stopped having any meaning for me when I heard Phillip's voice.

"Out." The flap flew up and the mist cleared. Fresh, breathable air rushed in. He grabbed my arm and dragged me outside. I tried to stand but could not. He walked towards the stream, half dragging me, and we both fell gratefully into it. A mist of steam rose off us as we entered the water. I swear I recall the water boiled with bubbles for an instant when we both immersed ourselves. The water was deliciously frigid and fresh on my steam-burned skin. I stuck my head all the way under against the sand, held it under for a long cooling moment, then surfaced. I could still feel the heat radiating off my crown—and something else. I dunked again, and again and again....

Eventually we turned over on our backs and just kind of lay there in the stream. No one spoke. I frankly did not have the energy. The sunshine filtered softly through the boughs of the cottonwoods. Rays beamed down at me, dappling the water into a glittering surface of refracted light that played against the white and brown tree trunks. The gurgling of the stream and sighing of the branches lulled me into a sublime level of relaxation I had not experienced since I was a small boy ... laying on the grass and looking up at the clouds with nothing to do and nowhere to go, just alive in the moment, feeling the grass and the breeze. I just lay there for the longest time letting the water cool my back and the sunlight warm my chest. The sky was a perfect cloudless blue. I felt like new. Fresh and content.

"*Ulsen bi naadidzoolhi,*" Phillip said. He stood up, went to the lodge and pulled on his clothes.

"What'd you say?" I followed in slow, slow motion. I pulled on my clothes but in extra slow motion. Every movement was a major effort. It took a half an hour to get dressed. By then the dry desert air had completely evaporated off me and my clothes.

"The breath of God. Live steam. Here drink." He handed me the water jug again. This time I tilted it over my elbow like a hillbilly drinking moonshine. I followed him back into the duplex.

He pulled a couple more Pendletons off the sofa, folded them up and tossed them in front of me.

"Sit on those." I slowly shifted over to them. It was as if I was trying to move through molasses. "Yup," he said, looking at me move in slow motion, "I think we have adequately weakened you physically. Time to access the spiritual."

I nodded and limped onto the blankets. It took the last bit of strength I had.

"Now pay attention, gopher hunter. Sit up straight in man seat, left leg underneath you, tuck your chin, straighten your spine, let your eyes relax and be unfocused. That means they'll go three quarters closed." I did as he said. My eyelids relaxed. I tucked my chin.

"Watch your breathing. Don't think. If a thought comes, just label it as a thought and let it go. Relax and let go of all the muscles except your back, bowels and groin. Begin a breath cycle of equal intervals. Inhale, pause, exhale, pause, and repeat the cycle."

Phillip droned on and on as I began to concentrate on my breathing. My breathing slowed and, just as I noticed it, he spoke.

"Good. Now slow your heart. First count the number of beats per one section of breath cycle, for example on the inhalation, then don't try and make anything happen. You probably have five or six per inhalation. Just feel your heartbeat slow. Feel your pulse first in your temples, then in your chest. Now in your wrist, now in your thumbs. Feel the pulse in your thighs. Now feel your entire body gently rock and sway with the pulse of your heartbeat."

It did. I could feel it. First in my thumbs, thighs and temples, but eventually, finally I became very, very still. More still than I had ever been since birth. So still that I could feel my entire body rock slightly like a boat in the waters of my own blood pumped by the engine of my heart.

"*Ow,* now just sit and watch your breathing. Become like the swinging door on a saloon. Now you breathe in, pause, now you breathe out, pause...."

His voice was always rich and deep like some fine whiskey, but now it lulled me and faded as my breath came in slow motion, and my heart pumped with fewer and longer beats. Time slowed and my awareness and world closed. My heartbeat slowed in my chest. I felt my body rock gently to the pulse of my heart. My breath came in slow even waves. My mind became quiet. And finally I just let go of my outer body. I just released ownership of it and attachment to it. It was as if my body died, but my sentience, my soul, remained deep inside somewhere. A bit of drool oozed from my mouth.

Then I smelled it. A pungent, aromatic scent of something burning. I felt the smoke gently caress my head and shoulders like the lightest touch of a woman. Suddenly I saw vivid tendrils of rich, purple light that twisted and turned, brightened and faded. Wisps of purple light interspersed and pulsed with a deeper center shaded into violet. At times the whole of the scene throbbed, deepening from purple to violet and tinged with orange tendrils of ether, with the beat of my heart, the cycle of my breath—and even something more. But I wasn't seeing with my eyes. My eyes I realized were nearly completely closed. I was seeing something else, from somewhere else in some other new way. I watched as the images continued to shift and change. "Maybe," I thought to myself, "that's where that song 'Purple Haze' got its name." Then I realized I was thinking and returned to watching.

Just then an immense, sharp, brilliant white light pierced my mind, stabbed into my head, and exploded outward from the center of my vision at light speed. It was as if I had just witnessed the Big Bang close up. I jerked back involuntarily. The sheer white stars faded outward into the edges of my vision. It was like watching the monitor on a *Star Trek* episode.

My body shuddered again in a way totally alien to me. I realized I had not breathed in a long time. I took a long, slow, deep inhalation of air. I exhaled just as slowly, trying to regain my breathing cycle. My heart was pumping so I began to watch it slow again. And shortly it began to slow again. Now I heard an enormous, deep, bass drum beat thunder against my chest and shake my body and entire being. It thundered again and I felt the diaphragm within me shudder in matching vibration.

The thunder struck again and my whole being shook with the impact, vibrating deep inside the center of me, beyond my body, further inside than even the center of my heart—to something else, that whispered and shuddered deep, deep within me and responded softly, lightly and nearly imperceptibly to the beat.

Thunder struck again and, as the deep bass faded, my voice, of its own volition, joined and replaced the rolling thunder in a long, low monotone of extended breath outward. My body rocked gently forward and back like a boat in its mooring, and my moan faded slowly away like a summer breeze.

My diaphragm vibrated outward to and through the rest of my body and I trembled in every extremity. My voice continued as deep as the drum, until my breath faded too, but slower than I would have imagined and longer than I would have anticipated.

I watched from a place high and deep inside my head as my body slowly eased out the final notes of its long, low, wordless song. It, or rather I, finally stopped. But I still trembled and rocked. And the quiet was exquisite in its completeness.

Then slowly, almost regretfully, I heard the breeze through the open window, gently sighing in the mesquite branches near the house. I heard them creep and crackle ever so slightly, even though it was spring and they were full of sap. I heard some kind of insect I could not see—its legs scrambling loudly in the dry, hard dirt. A bird flew by—I could tell because I heard the beats of its wings in the air. Then all was quiet again.

And I was still, still as death. My breathing faded so that even I could barely notice it. My pulse was slight and slow. And then I heard it. At first I thought it was a ringing in my ears from the other sounds. But this was different. It was a high, all encompassing, soundless sound. It was a primordial tone without pitch, beyond description and outside the range my ears were designed to detect.

I was an avid diver and I had long ago learned to listen for the cracklings of the reef, being destroyed by waves and eaten by parrot fish. Once you heard it, it was an under-sound that permeated everything in the ocean. This was like that, only more so. It was a non-sound that deafened me with its silent roar.

It was as if I could hear the very particles and waves of the fabric of the universe whirling and clashing around each other simultaneously attracted and repelled in an endless dance of cosmic life and death. The roar faded as an even stranger phenomena enveloped me. I was already high and deep within myself, ensconced safely away in the hollow recesses of my head. But I still oriented my frame of reference and point of view out the front of my face where my unseeing eyes sat.

Yet suddenly I began to drift upwards. I looked for something to hold onto, but I had long since let go of any control over my limbs. My left leg was dead numb asleep underneath my right, as were my hands. I could see a single ant crawling on my bare arm but no longer felt it.

With a jolt I realized I was observing it from upside down! And I was continuing to drift upwards and out of my head, like some child's birthday balloon that had lost its mooring. My stomach looped and I felt a dizzying wave of vertigo overcome me.

I was now well six feet over my own head and looking down on myself! I could see everything in a glowing, white, shimmering luminosity—just like the glow I had seen around Phillip, my professor, and fellow students. Everything was there, but everything glowed in a strange kind of luminous vision.

Now I was upright but slightly canted left, but I began rolling sideways then...

"Back now, *shiye*, that's enough." Phillip's voice echoed faintly into the hollow, empty halls of my mind. "Break the straight brace-line of your spine and relax." I did so slowly. My breath began to quicken, and my heart.

I shuddered, coughed and swallowed. Drool dripped from my mouth and I wiped it away worried that Phillip would see.

"Sorry," I said.

Phillip shook his head. "No, that's good. You let go of the physical just as you should. You are doing great."

"Great?"

"Let's go back outside." He stood up and walked out. I slowly climbed up on ancient legs and wobbled out the door.

"What happened?" I managed to speak. Phillip handed me a water bottle and I took a long, slow swig. The sun was going down. Somehow it was hours later.

"You tell me. But first build a fire," Phillip said casually. "It's going to be a long night."

But what about the coals from the earlier fire," I asked.

"Out and cold coals. But check." He walked back into the house. I began rubbing my numb legs with my numb hands. My body was on fire with surging blood and I was very tired. I took another swig of water. Finally I screwed up the energy to move to the fire and check it. But as usual Phillip was right. The fire was completely out and without live coals.

I looked around until I found a dry straight stick and a curved piece of old dead wood. Then I grabbed a handful of dry grass and crushed it up and placed it in the curve as tinder.

I searched about again and picked up a sharp stone and briefly hollowed out the curved wood to fit the tip of the long stick. I squatted down, placed both feet on the curved wood and started to spin the long stick as a fire drill.

I was at it for about five minutes, furiously spinning the drill stick without even a glimmer of smoke when Phillip came back out of the house, carrying one of the kitchen chairs, and a Pendleton blanket. He stopped and stared for a long moment. Then he put the chair down, sat in it, and tossed the blanket in front of me.

"What," he said in a neutral voice, "are you doing?"

"You said to build a fire, so I am trying to build a fire."

He fished in his jeans and tossed me a lighter. I caught it.

"If you need to build a fire, use a lighter. That's the most practical way to do it today." Then he leaned forward and gave me one of those transfixing looks. "But if you need to build a man, train the boy. Spiritual training is still the most practical training in the world. If you have a strong spiritual base, and a connection to *Ulsen*, then you can overcome anything. Because your spiritual base will always allow you to build upon, customize, improvise, or modify your physical self. That," he looked at me intently, "is the easy part."

I took the lighter. I started to wonder what the hard part could be but got distracted when Phillip handed me some tinder. I lit it with the lighter then fed the flames with twigs. Phillip walked off and retuned with kindling. I fed that in as well and the fire started to burn steadily.

Phillip walked off and returned again, this time with an armful of split wood. He tossed it next to the fire and sat down. I realized he was giving me time to collect myself and my strength. We both stared into the flames in silence for a long time.

"I know you are tired, but it is important to review your training now while the track is fresh. Ready?"

"Training, that was training?"

"Of course. That was manhood training."

"How so?"

"Apache physical skills were keen. Our ability to hunt, stalk game, steal horses was legendary. Ulzana once killed two deer with one arrow. Nana took a horse from an American while he slept with the reins in his hands." He closed his eyes remembering.

"Our men regularly outran the cavalry's horses. They could cover fifty miles a day on foot. The boys, they learned to run four miles with water in their mouths, to bring to their wounded, and to learn how to breathe as you just were. But physical skills were not enough. No Apache could be a whole man without a spiritual side, without having *diyi*...."

"Power," I said, wanting him to know I was paying attention. He nodded.

"We had to be able to fight when we had no weapons, heal when there were no medicines, and find game when all had fled. To do that," his right hand moved outward from his chest in a line, "one must have *diyi*."

"And that is what I was seeing, the luminosity around everyone?"

"Yes, in *Ndee* it is *diyi*. In English it is also power, but electromagnetic bioluminescent power. That which is symptomatic of *Ulsen*."

"But how, how did they do that?"

"They developed what you would call today inner technologies, as all indigenous peoples do. Non-Indians change their environment in wonderful ways. Electricity to light the night, cement floors to keep the worms out of the kids bellies, penicillin for infection." He drew in the dirt with a stick.

"You know, I went down to Nicaragua once to a Pan-Indian conference. They live the old hard way there. Some of the Misquito people, they still walk around nude but not naked; they have their man and womanhood cords draped over their genitals. But the bugs and living conditions were so hard. Even for me. Anyway, Indians, they change themselves. You use a telescope or a microscope to see better close or far away, right?"

"Sure, that's way better than eyes alone."

"Sometimes. Depends on what you're looking to see."

"Uh— don't follow." It was a phrase I would mutter many times over the years with Phillip.

"The light from the stars. When you look at the stars through a telescope, is it seeing the stars now as they are?"

"Well, no, it's old."

"How old?"

"Tens of thousands of years."

"And when you look at some microbe under the microscope, are you seeing it as it is, or squashed and separated from its environment—like some kind of cartoon?"

He put his arms out, one up one down, turned his head to the side and stuck out his tongue. He looked and I laughed. I stopped to see if he would become angry since I had laughed at him. But he was laughing too.

Later on the reservations I would see him make the kids laugh in exactly the same way and then gather them around him to shoot some arrows as he called it. Teach them a truth through a subtle old Apache story. I saw him do it many times, and it worked every time, including this time.

"Now you look like road kill." I laughed.

"You should see me after ceremony," he shot back smiling.

"Have you ever done this before? Trained somebody like me, like this?"

"No, never, and I never will again. You're it, so pay attention. We don't have much time—maybe a couple of years. No more questions from you now. I need to ask you some."

"Shoot," I said. But in the back of my mind I stored away "not much time."

"Never say that to an Apache." He smiled at me intensely. I looked back soberly. I knew the Apaches were renowned worldwide as warriors. In the old days no one ever even saw them. They were just suddenly shot from one of the impenetrable natural rock fortresses that abounded in the Arizona desert.

I remember having read one account where a vaquero out on a wide open plain sensing danger had dismounted, drawn and cocked both pistols and walked forward of his mount to check things out. Silent and sudden, an Apache covered in the dust that matched the desert floor had risen at his feet and grasped both of his six gun barrels, greeting him and laughing. The encounter ended friendly but the message was clear. And the vaquero evidently never forgot it.

"Hey, you awake?" Phillip called out. I came out of my reverie. Phillip's eyes were smiling.

"Well, I'm more awake than before," I said, trying my hand at speaking Indian idiom.

"Yes, you are," Phillip nodded. "Now what happened first?"

"Hmm, well then, the drum beat—it kind of matched my heart beat. Then something really wild happened. I kind of shrank inside myself. I became like a little ball of light. And I sank into the floor. So what does it all mean?" I looked at Phillip.

"Do you feel that your physical body shrank and went into the floor?" He looked back.

"No, of course not."

"Then if it was not physical, what was it?"

"Spiritual. Something, some part of me that was spiritual."

Phillip nodded slowly and put a hand to his jaw. "So if what defines you as you, your focus of attention, your place of awareness, went deep inside your form, what was it?"

"I don't know. Tell me."

"Never. No man tells another what to do or think. Okay, let's move on. What happened next?"

"Then I sat up on the blankets. I relaxed my muscles, then I slowed my breathing, then I slowed my heart just like before only more so this time. Then—"

"That is called battle breath because it is to calm one's heart and soul in combat," Phillip said. "Go on."

"Then I smelled the sage you burned." Phillip picked up the abalone shell. It was filled with dirt and on top of that were some fading coals from the fire. On top of that were the charred remains of the sage stick I had seen earlier.

"Yes, I held this pipe sage under your nose. I blessed you with it, with a cross and circle. Sage is like a spiritual antiseptic, helps you clear your mind of thoughts, open up, drop ego."

"It smelled good, the sage; it relaxed me even more, true. But something else happened. I saw colors and shades of vivid violet and purple; they just came and kept appearing and morphing. Like the same kind of light show from *2001: A Space Odyssey.*"

"Ever seen anything like that before?"

"No, never, what was it?"

"You tell me."

"I have no idea."

"Seen violet anywhere else recently?" he asked. I thought for a moment.

"On the lance—of course, the purple, the violet—you mean I was going beyond the visible spectrum of light with human eyes to the invisible—to ultraviolet!" I jumped up and grabbed his arm. He laughed quietly, nodding.

"I didn't say anything. You did it, you figured it out and you said it. And that's what a real man does—figures out the mysteries of the world—physical and spiritual."

"But you said that was also like an antiseptic, so that must have helped open me even more."

"How about that."

"That's truly amazing. So that's what you meant about microscopes and telescopes."

"What is more sophisticated," he asked, "the latest computer—or this?" He tapped his head.

"That," I said, starting to point with my hand and then using my chin. He nodded.

"Then from which would you expect to get the most sophisticated results?"

"This," I tapped my own head, "makes sense."

"But you are forgetting something else, aren't you?" He looked at me with that patient, but bemused expression on his face.

"Like what?"

"Like that you just told me that you saw a smell."

"That's right, I forgot."

"Ever done that before?"

"No, how did that happen?"

"As you become still and quiet and open, you open yourself up to the very real, but mostly unnoticed spiritual realm. You are like someone in a car at night. The headlights are on, so you can only see in the beams, nothing else; the radio is on, so you can only hear the music; the windows are up, so you cannot smell the air." He stood up and walked slowly clockwise around the fire and tossed a small split log on. "But if you stop the car, you begin to hear the night sounds; if you turn off the lights, your visual purple rods...."

"Purple again," I interjected.

"Yes, purple again, the color of royalty, because it signifies connection to the divine."

He shook his finger gently at me. "Good point, I knew you were the right one. Anyway, you start looking out the corner of your eye where there are more visual purple rods, your night vision will come out quick; if the moon is full, it will become almost as bright as day if you stay out long enough. Then you squat down." He did so.

"And look up at the horizon and you will see even better. Then if you turn off that crazy music with lyrics that are outrageous and designed to make you think about shooting your mother, or whatever, then you can stop thinking bad thoughts, empty out, come to center."

Clearly he was describing something he had done on many occasions. "Then you wet your nostrils." He wet his thumb on his tongue then wiped the bottom of his nose with it. "So you can smell better by catching the molecules in the air on the moist surface. Cup your ears, so you can hear like the deer." He cupped his ears with both hands. "Then you can know the night. But as soon as you restart that car, turn on those headlights and radio, then the world is only what you can see in your headlights." Phillip stood up and stretched his long frame.

"So for the first time in my life, I'm turning off the car?" I threw another log on the fire. Sparks crackled and flew up in the darkening night sky. I followed their flight upwards until they met the emerging evening stars, and pretty soon I could not separate spark from star.

"Well, once my breathing and heart slowed way down and muscles were relaxed, I could feel my heartbeat throbbing all over, and I could even feel my body rocking back and forward with the heartbeat."

"And what people rock back and forth when they pray?"

"Orthodox Jews."

"A covenant people. So might they rock as a physical memory of spiritual experience from their covenant tradition?"

"Yes."

"And did the rocking help create a vibration in you?"

"Yes, sir, it sure did."

"What are the sounds our words make when we communicate?"

"Vibrations! I get it. We are getting good vibes. No—God vibes!" I was pleased with myself.

Phillip rolled his eyes and shook his head sadly. "No, you don't. This is Arizona not California. Indians are not hippies. They are patriotic; they like guns and serve their country in the military."

"But that makes sense, doesn't it?" I asked.

"Does it to you?" Phillip shot back.

"Yes." I nodded.

"That is the important thing. Remember, one tells a child what to do to keep them safe, like 'don't touch the fire.' But if, as a free man, you want to put your hand in the fire, that's your business. What next?"

I looked back at Phillip. Somehow he had moved across the fire from my chair and sat back down, with me never noticing. His ability to seemingly appear and disappear at will was just one of the things about Phillip that always amazed me.

"How do you do that?" I asked.

"I'm asking the questions here, gopher killer," he said. "What happened next?"

"Then I became very quiet and very high and deep up inside my head."

"You mean that the center of your sentience emanated from deep within your head?"

"Uh huh, that's exactly what I was about to say, professor," I dead-panned.

"Good, I knew passing up that teaching position at Harvard was worth it."

"Ah, I remember next, there was an explosion of white light outward—it was like when they went to hyper-drive in *Star Wars.*"

Phillip brought a strange, brass, carved bell out in one hand and a matching, ornately-carved striker. He held them up.

"This is a Tibetan bell and *dorje* for striking it. The *dorje* is carved to represent a diamond thunderbolt of enlightenment."

"Like what just happened with me?"

"A bit like what just happened to you."

He gently struck the bell with the *dorje* and an elegant, clear, high-pitched tone filled the air. It was impossible to think over the tone. The pulse cut the very air and lingered, and only reluctantly, ceased. For a moment all was silent. Then sounds of night returned gradually.

"Nice," I said, "but I don't get it."

"I struck this in front of your forehead, much harder than that."

"When?"

"When you saw the white light explosion."

"But," I stumbled, "I never heard anything."

"But, you saw it, didn't you? You saw color?"

"Yeah … I guess I did that."

"Scientists call that synesthesia—a mixing of the senses."

"Wasn't that a Disney movie?" Phillip ignored me. But I was cracking myself up.

"When you let go of holding onto perceiving reality through the gateways of your physical form—eyes, ears, touch—and experience reality not limited by physicality, then literally, the realms of your reality shift."

"So I experienced that vibration of sound as a vibration of light?"

"And isn't light a symptom of energy, just like heat? Aren't we primarily sighted beings, with most of our sensory input coming through our vision? So doesn't it make sense that since vision is your primary sensory input—it dominates your perception, whether in the physical or spiritual realms?"

I nodded slowly. We both gazed into the fire, hypnotized by the flames, the heat, and the crackling.

"So what happened after the explosion?"

I thought back. "So anyway, then the strangest thing happened. I began to rise above and out of my body. It was wild!"

"Aren't you forgetting something?"

"Like what?"

"Did you rise straight up or did you start to twist off and tumble?" he asked slightly impatiently.

"I did, how did you know—when I forgot?" He amazed me yet again. I was getting tired of this.

"Because I saw you," he said simply.

"Yeah, I did. I rose above myself. And then I began to cant to the—"

"Left?" he asked lazily.

"Yeah! How did you know that?"

"I already told you, I saw you. But the real question is, what part of you rose above the other part of you?"

"Well, since the physical part of me—my body—didn't go anywhere, it had to be the spiritual part of me."

He nodded, "What part would it be that contained your perspective and self-awareness? That, when it left the body, no longer needed to conform to the body's orientation? Didn't you feel round, spherical?"

"I did, yeah, that's incredible. So if it was the part of me that is me, then, no, are you saying that my soul left my body?"

"I keep telling you. No man tells another what to do. I'm not telling you anything."

But the conclusion was obvious to me. "But I know you're right."

"How do you know?"

"Because I felt it happen, I experienced it. I know it to be true."

"Know the definition of faith?"

"No, what?"

"Faith is the wisdom of things unseen. Except now—"

"Now I'm starting to see them." I finished his sentence.

"And thus, gaining that wisdom."

"So you are saying that wisdom is not just intellectual, but it's an actual body of knowledge concerning the workings of the luminous, spiritual world?"

"Very well said." The fire flared on its own as if to agree on cue. Phillip's face was like gold leather in its reflection.

"So you've been to Tibet too?" I asked.

"Nope. Like to go though. But I have met with some Tibetan Buddhist monks. They gave me the bell and *dorje.* We have lots in common. Like us, they have holy ground, sand paintings; they value turquoise; their boots even have the turned up toe pieces. Some of our words are even the same."

Many years later after Phillip's death, I would learn from his sister, Pansy, that the monks had come to pay their respects and gifted him the bell and *dorje* to honor the most famous Apache holy man of his time—known even to spiritual masters in Tibet. But back then I knew nothing of that and he never mentioned it.

"Back to work. What happened next?"

"I felt looser then, less connected to my body, I guess, now that I start to understand all of this a bit more. Then I felt and heard the drum beats. It shook me completely. My diaphragm vibrated just like the skin of the drum." I pointed to the small drum with the curved drumstick sitting on top of it.

"Actually I use this Tarahumara drum." Phillip pulled a large round drum out from behind his chair. "That Apache water drum doesn't work so well for this stuff."

"What's all this Tibetan and Tarahumara stuff got to do with Apache tradition?"

"The Lakota have a wonderful prayer, '*Aho, mitakuoye oyasin.*' They say it when they go into the purification lodge. It means 'For all my relations.' I do this hard thing not for myself but for everyone that I am related to, the two-legged, four-legged, finned, winged, including the Tibetans and the Tarahumara. And to answer your question—nothing. I am not teaching you Apache ways, that is my tradition."

"Then what are you teaching me?"

"Don't know yet. Probably won't ever know. Maybe you won't even know in your lifetime. I am teaching you how things really are. I know how the Apache utilized this wisdom to survive. But, you have to figure out how you will use it, what for and to whom."

"So this is not just for the Apache?"

"We are the custodians of this way, the subject matter experts, but not the owners. We are all connected on the hoop. Man needs woman, woman needs man. But no free man can own another. Black peoples needs white folks, white needs red, red needs yellow. Everyone has their duties and their expertise as a people and a nation, but we don't own it. All of humanity owns it. And we are charged to share it, so that the next human being can benefit from it, survive because of it." He poked the fire.

"Course, so far you're the only one interested." We both smiled.

"Not very good odds, huh?"

"Been waiting on you to show up for a long time. Almost gave up, started thinking nobody would, and I'd have nobody to pass this on to. I got high hopes for you."

"I'll do my best."

"Then tell me about the drum beat."

"The drum beat I heard. I felt it in my chest, especially in my diaphragm, because it's like this drum." I picked up the Tarahumara drum. The goat hide membrane was about twenty-four inches wide and stretched over a cottonwood frame. I held it parallel to my chest. "I felt it in my diaphragm the same way. It loosened me somehow from—from my body, and then for some reason I moaned or chanted with the drum beat—like I was trying to match the reverberation. I breathed out in that long, low tone for a long time—but I don't know why. Do you?" Phillip looked at me.

"Still expecting answers to your questions. A man figures out his own answers. And there are no easy ones. Everything you are learning now, you will not understand right away. It may be years before you are able to understand all that you learn here and now, and years more before you need to use it. But eventually you will need it. *Ulsen* only gives you what is needed for the task, never more. And by the end you will be rung out."

"Sounds cheery." I grinned.

"You have no idea," he grinned, "but remember, you'll find out. Ever heard Indian songs?"

"Yes, sir. I've been to a pow-wow or two."

"That's right, I forgot. I'm getting senile in my old age. Indian songs are monotone, because they are designed to eliminate thought, so we can drop the individual ego that separates us from God. So are songs and dances purposefully monotonous."

He stood up and began walking slowly clockwise around the fire, in a slow demonstration of Apache dance step. The fire seemed to follow him as the wind whipped it.

"The Jews, then the Christians, then finally the Muslims—they too, like the Apache, are all people of the desert and the mountains. The desert cleans and purifies us, and the mountains elevate us to the spiritual. They all are also people of the same Book—Torah, Old Testament, Koran, the same Word, and they read the word, say the word, think about the word, and the word keeps them on path—the words give them rules and laws."

He circled the fire again, now turning at the quarter of it, making circles within a circle.

"But we did not have words and books and laws. Our way was to do the impeccable thing, not the moral one. We had no police, no judges, and no soldiers. We worked and lived together not by artificial rules and laws but natural, impeccable action. We learned to become quiet, open up and hear *Ulsen's* echoes, *Bichi'eke'hada'an's* power."

"Bichi—" I stuttered.

"Life-Giver, another name for *Ulsen*. But no man tells another what to do, or how to think. So you can say *Ulsen*, you can say God, the divine, the force like in *Star Wars*—whatever you want to call him-her-it. But it is more than just male or female."

"Bob," I said, "How about Bob? I like Bob," I said. I was cracking myself up again.

"Keep that sense of humor. It will come in handy later. When the warriors have a hard time, or are wounded, they would smile and joke, especially around the women and children, so as not to alarm them but reassure them."

"There's something else. I heard something in the silence, a non-sound, like a soundless sound—underneath all the other, normal sounds, it was a constant, perfect pitch, like …"

"Most people only hear the artificial, man-made sounds around them. They are inundated by their own din. Did you know that if asked to hum something, the majority of folks will hum something in B natural?"

"Nope, and what is B natural?"

"It is the same tone as the current of electricity pulsing all around you, through those power lines there." He pointed to some power lines. "To those lines there." He pointed at some trees.

"I see," I said, not seeing at all. "But I don't get the trees as power lines."

"Have you tried seeing them?"

"No, sir."

"Then maybe you should. But, back to what you heard or didn't hear. Was it like a sound underlying all sound? Like a cosmic song, the universe itself is singing?" Phillip said.

"Yes, like that." I nodded. "Maybe…like…angel song."

"Practice what you have learned here tonight for the next three months."

"Three months?"

"Three months. I've got to take a trip anyway. While I'm away, fast, to further weaken your physical—"

"To access the spiritual," I interjected.

"Yes, but don't interrupt—it's rude. Real men are respectful and thus receive respect. Good manners bring good heart, good heart brings good soul, good soul brings goodness to all relations. First month, fast one week per month; second month, twice—two weeks per month—one week on, the next off; third month, three weeks, and fourth, the whole month. The first day of the week, three meals, second two, third one, fourth juice, Friday water only."

"That's pretty harsh," I said.

His eyes became flinty and dark. The firelight danced inside them.

"Life is hard. Apache men learned to become harder. Harder than the desert, harder than the mountains. Harder than the rocks. Because we were here when they were soft. But even then, we were hard. This is the burden of manhood. Bear your burdens quietly without complaint. Listen to others to see how you can help those who are not as strong as you. Sometimes just listening will help."

I was finally beginning to experience the famous Apache stoic tradition. Their Spartan ways had first attracted me to them. As I had spent time with Phillip, I had seen little of this side of him.

But now it began to emerge, but in a totally unexpected context. The Apache superhuman stamina, their ferocious physicality, their reputation as the tigers of the American Southwest—it all emerged entirely from their spiritual perspective. But Phillip was still talking.

"Become humble. Be quiet. Listen to people. Open up. Let go of your point of view. Don't think about your point of view. Don't judge. Just listen. Don't think of your own response while they talk. Just…listen. And before you answer, pause. In case they have something else to add. No drinking, no smoking, and no fooling around with your girl."

He paused and looked at me. I remained silent.

"Good. That's better. You know Indians are quiet. The country ones, the cowboys and the ones who still live up in the mountains and outside, they won't look you in the eyes when they meet you. They don't want to be rude. And it may be several days before they talk directly to you and several more before they know you well enough to formally introduce themselves. They take time to respect people. You must learn to do the same." Phillip looked at me.

"This is your pure time, your spiritual childhood. Now the real, adult spiritual world unfolds before you. Childhood ends. Your boy's life is over. Manhood begins."

"Now pay attention gopher hunter."

Don't worry if you don't have access to a sweat lodge or a stand of willows to build one—not to mention lava rocks, firewood and a stream. By tradition only quested men can pour water in a lodge anyway. Also check with your doc first. Make sure you are healthy enough for sweating.

Then just use the steam or sauna at your gym, or just turn your shower on hot and sit just outside the stall with the bathroom door closed and a towel against the opening on the floor. Make sure you hydrate—drink, drink, drink. If you feel faint, STOP and open the door. The first rule of training is living through it.

Pre-position sage, sweetgrass or just a sliver of cedar and some matches where you will sit. If you are in a small apartment, then quarter the sage stick or sweetgrass braid so as to not set off the smoke detector. Make sure the sage or whatever is sitting on something inflammable such as the earth in a potted plant. Burning down your apartment is not part of the program.

Sit up straight in man seat, left leg underneath you, tuck your chin, straighten your spine, let your eyes relax unfocused.

Watch your breathing.

Don't think. If a thought comes, just label it as a thought and let it go.

Relax and let go of all the muscles except your back, bowels and groin.

Begin a breath cycle of equal intervals. Inhale, pause, exhale, pause, and repeat the cycle.

Now slow your heart. First count the number of beats per one section of breath cycle, for example on the inhalation, then repeat the practice for each cycle.

Don't try and make anything happen. Just feel your heartbeat slow.

Feel it first in your temples, then in your chest.

Now in your wrist, now in your thumbs. Feel the pulse in your thighs.

Now feel your entire body rock and sway with the pulse of your heart.

Now breathe in.

Pause.

Now breathe out.

Pause.

With your eyelids still relaxed, light the sage.

Return to watching your breathing.

When you are finished, or you return to sentience, relax your back, secure the burning sage and jot a note down of what you remember happening. Don't intellectualize the experience. Just write what you recall.

Did your breath slow?

Did your heart slow?

Did you see smell?

Did your point of view shift?

Did you lose self-awareness?

Don't worry if everything didn't work for you. Don't worry if you don't understand everything that happened. Figuring it all out comes later, sometimes many years later. But understanding will come, and when you need it most.

CHILDHOOD'S END

Nothing must ever be done to harm the children.
—First Rule of Warriorship

WE SAT TALKING BY THE FIRE till sun up. I went home at dawn and slept that day and night. From then on I was never the same.

College became secondary. I was studying fine arts, water color, sculpture, but my academic interest paled in comparison to my classes with Phillip. My art became much more spiritually themed though, and focused on Apache subject matter almost exclusively. It still is, forty years later. I still went to class. But class became a vehicle for my training with Phillip.

Lectures were great for practicing luminous vision. I quickly learned there was much more to see. And each new visionary experience was more incredible than the last. Whenever a teacher would move about the stage during a lecture, after a couple of seconds, I could clearly make out a luminous shape remaining behind where the professor had stood.

But after a couple of more moments, the shape would follow the physical form of the professor and slowly merge with him. It was an amazing discovery and I delighted in seeing professors, both physical and luminous, move about the lecture stage. I couldn't wait to tell Phillip. But I opened up in other unexpected ways too.

I started to get to know students from different college departments, people that I would have never talked to, from different social classes. And because of these new-found friendships, I established a second, double major in political science, thanks to

75

the help of a gay fine arts faculty advisor, again someone I would have never spoken to before Phillip's instructions.

Meals were ideal for listening. I got to know waiters and waitresses I would have never spoken to, much less learned anything about. One lunch stood out. My waitress was just past middle-age and I asked her how she was.

"Oh, so-so I guess." She poured me more water.

"Why just so-so, it's a beautiful day?"

"Well, yes, I guess it is. I just—nothing, dear." Her timid answer was almost drowned out in the din of the coed feeding frenzy. She started to leave. I remembered Phillip's words, to really listen to people, just listen, everywhere and anytime. I was already late for a class I hated anyway.

"No, please, ma'am, what is it?"

"Well, I—had a baby a long time ago, before I was married, then I got divorced."

"And what happened to her?"

"Him, he was the prettiest little baby boy; well, I gave him up, you see, for adoption, and well, today's his birthday. I guess I was just thinking about him, wondering where he's at now, what he's like." She looked up and out the plate glass window into another time and another place.

"You know," I said quietly, "that's quite a coincidence. Because I was given up for adoption myself. Course today's not my birthday. But I often wonder about my birth mother, if she ever thinks about me."

She put her hand on my arm gently. I looked up at her. She was quiet for a long time, but I just kept listening even in the silence. Finally she opened her mouth and spoke.

"Well, honey, don't you ever think that she doesn't think about you on your birthday and every day. Because, honey, she does." Her eyes misted up and she managed a little smile before she quickly moved off to the next table. I never saw her again.

As the months sped by, I spent less and less time in the cafeteria. By the time Phillip returned I was ten pounds leaner. My circle of friends and acquaintances had tripled. My temper was better and I was less impatient. My pace had slowed, my understanding grown. I was quiet and humble. I walked close to the walls in the hall to stay unnoticed and out of the way.

And I could see: everywhere and all the time, at the literal blink of an eye. Everything glowed. Everything had a luminous halo around it. And there was more. I remember when I sat down in Phillip's little kitchen to tell him about everything that had happened.

"There's luminosity around everyone and everything." He smiled and I continued. "But there is also this luminous body that follows the physical one around. I mean it is amazing. It has the same height and shape of the person's body."

"So what is that?" he asked.

"I knew you would ask, so I have thought about it a lot," I said.

"Don't think; see, listen, feel and then know the answer intuitively and impeccably." Phillip stirred a savory smelling pot on the stove.

"Knew you'd say that. So I have been working on this, especially at night. And I figured it out. I use my physical body all day. But at night I have to sleep. And while I sleep, I must dream—I have to have REM sleep, rapid eye movement dream sleep. And this is what that luminous body is. It's my dreaming body!"

Phillip nodded proudly. "And that is why dreams are so important to all Indian peoples. Because it's one half of our beings, our selves. Indians look at whites as very clever, but children. They are half-asleep or half-dead. In Ndee we say we are the living, and the non-Indian we call *ndaa*—the dead. Because while the non-Indian is clever at making microscopes and electricity and cement floors, he knows nothing of the spiritual side of himself. That is why he is always lost. He never feels at home, no matter where he is at. He thinks always that he is separate from everything and everybody, even from his own soul."

"But that's not all," I said.

I looked out the kitchen window, and relaxed the focus of my vision. In the distance the Santa Ritas mountain range stood out a deeper blue than the bright blue of the Arizona sky. As I relaxed into peripheral vision, the bright neon of an even more intense blue popped into sight, like God turning on the neon lights.

"I can see the luminosity around the Ritas."

"*Ow,*" Phillip replied with the Ndee affirmative.

"But that means the mountains have a spirit too. It means they are alive. And I see the same thing on the rocks, and trees and everywhere on everything."

"Spirit is an energy being without physical form. What you are referring to are things that have physical form but also possess a spiritual essence. We have dancers that specialize in impersonating the mountain spirits."

"You mean a soul?"

"That's what it's called." He set a steaming plate of traditional Apache stew down in front of me. The venison, peppers and corn tasted like heaven. Having fasted that week, I tore into it. Phillip smiled at my enthusiasm.

"You are saying that those mountains, these trees, even those rocks, each and every one of them have a soul?"

"I didn't, but you did. And that is certainly the traditional Ndee perspective. Everything has soul and everything is alive."

"Even rocks?"

"Especially rocks. Rocks move. When they are lava, they flow and glow. When we heat them up in the lodge, they crack and talk. But the rest of the time, when they are cold, they sleep. Like grizzlies in winter, they hibernate."

I absorbed this in silence. Even the rocks were alive; even they had spirit.

"So is that why all the Indians fought so hard for their land. Why they refused to sell it, to give it up, like even now I hear the Chiricauhuas are trying to buy a reservation out near Sunsites."

Phillip nodded slowly. "The Ndee were the last free, wild men. They refused to give up their land or their freedom. Geronimo finally surrendered after being tracked down by Chato and the Apache scouts in 1886. The Army, they could not keep up with Geronimo and his six warriors. But even then after his surrender, a small band fled into hiding in old Mexico."

He tapped the table lightly, remembering some unheard, ancient drum beat. His eyes took on a distant look. He too stared out at the mountains.

"We are a mountain people really. We live in the hoop of four sacred mountain ranges. The *Chokonen* Chiricauhua, called *Chihuicuai*, were the wildest and the freest of all of us. They were lead by Cochise, greatest of the great Apache chiefs. They fought for their freedom to the end; they fought for the soul of their land to the last. The United States government did not appreciate their resistance."

"That," he said tapping the table, "is why we have no reservation."

"We?" I asked.

"I," he sat up straighter, "am Chiricauhua."

We sat in silence then for a while.

"We used our seers to see the enemy before they were visible. We could see the Americans days before they could find us. There were just too many. And too few of us." He looked at me. "Stopped eating, huh, full?"

I wasn't, but something was bothering me now. "If this deer had a soul, then how can I eat it?"

Phillip stood up and disappeared into the bed room. After a couple of minutes he emerged with a simple wood bow and a fur quiver with several arrows inside.

"What's that fur?" I asked.

Phillip smiled. "*Nchoio*, mountain lion. It was my father's. Let's take a ride." We walked out and got into my Fiat.

"Head up to Oracle," he said. Then he was silent.

About a half an hour later we were on Oracle up in the foothills. Now it's all houses out there. But back then it was open, rolling ranch land.

"Turn west here," Phillip said. I took a dirt road and pulled up to a cattle bar and barbwire-hooked gate. Make sure you close it behind us." Phillip said, his battered old, straw cowboy hat down over his eyes. "Keep going till you run out of road." We bumped along for about the next forty minutes. I stopped and turned off the engine. The road had ended.

Phillip pushed his hat up, looked around and got out. He threw his hat back inside and picked up the bow and quiver. He stepped through the bow and deftly strung it. Then he handed me the quiver. I slung it over my shoulder.

"Not like that. That's the movie way. Like this." He shifted the quiver to my left front hip.

He drew an arrow. They were old-style cane arrows but with metal tips. He nocked with his index and middle fingers, and tilted the bow diagonally right to top to bottom left so the arrow rested on his left hand and the bow back.

"Stand straight like a warrior and face the enemy or the game, pull and push at the same time. Draw to your nose. See the target. Point with your nose and your left index finger."

His left index finger rose off the bow and pointed. There was a sudden "thung"—and the arrow shot out and buried itself in a barrel cactus, twenty feet away.

I gave a long, low whistle. Phillip turned. "That is nothing. In the old days we could put three arrows in the air simultaneously. We could take birds on the wing or pin them to the ground. Until the Americans got repeating Winchesters, we held them at bay with just two little sticks like these."

"Two sticks?" I questioned.

"There is a modern day archer that read the Army officers' journals that fought the Indians on the frontier. He decided to try and duplicate the archery feats that those Army men described. Guess how far he found Indians could hit a target the size of a plate with an arrow?"

"Seventy-five yards?" I asked.

Phillip smiled and shook his head.

"A hundred?" I really had no idea.

Phillip shook his head again.

"A hundred and fifty?" I guessed wildly.

Phillip shook his head again.

"I give up. How far?"

"Two hundred and fifty yards."

"That's impossible!" I exclaimed. "The Army qualifies with their M-16s only out to three hundred yards."

"That is precisely the point. Mechanical technology has its limits. But human inner technologies are limitless, and with training from childhood, a trained man is capable of the impossible. Now you try." He handed me the bow. I nocked an arrow, and aimed in, closing one eye.

"Leave both eyes open, don't pull—push the bow out and pull the string back as you bring it to your nose, then just let go."

There was "thung" and my arrow dropped at my feet. He picked it up and handed it back to me. There was no smirk, no smart remarks, no rebuke, and no impatience.

I re-nocked the arrow, aimed carefully and shot. This time the arrow zinged off in an arc to the left of the cactus. But it did stick in the ground.

"Mark the spot, so we'll get it later. Nock another," Phillip said levelly. I did. I drew even more carefully, aimed in and released. The arrow stuck just a foot ahead of the barrel cactus, quivering in the ground.

"Don't try so hard. It is a special non-effort, just like seeing." That rang a bell with me and made sense. I lightened up.

"Hold the bow and arrow as one. But lightly. Look at the cactus. Then see it. Then just release. Let the arrow go."

"Thung." The arrow was gone. I looked about totally dumbfounded. "Where'd it go?"

Phillip walked up to the cactus and put his hand between *two* arrows in the cactus.

"Better," was all Phillip said. No praise either.

I practiced with all seven arrows in the quiver. Then I collected them and at Phillip's direction shot them all again. This time four hit the cactus. I collected them all and shot again. That time six were in the barrel. On the fourth shoot all were in the cactus and Phillip seemed satisfied.

"Now we hunt."

He motioned for me to follow. We had only walked a few paces when he pointed to some tracks in the sand.

"Jack rabbit—see the pellets?" I did see the little rabbit dung. We walked over a small rise. "Follow the trail. See how it leads into the brush there?"

I nodded. He walked to the right.

"This jack will turn to the right, to elude predators, so we'll head to the right to cut the trail again." Sure enough we cut the trail.

"How'd you know he'd go to the right?"

"He was always leaning right, see?" I did. The tracks turned slightly right even when they were heading straight.

I followed Phillip who now seemed to walk even more gracefully and without sound. He moved in a slow, steady stalk, like a tree in the breeze. I realized such movement would not startle game and was wondering at the skill of it when Phillip stopped, put his index finger to his lips, then two fingers to his eyes and then slowly extended his arm pointing. I looked, and finally I saw the jack rabbit, much bigger than I imagined with enormous ears sitting very still about thirty feet away.

Phillip motioned me forward and he advanced, but to the side, flanking the animal. The jack's head turned in response to Phillip's course. I kept one eye on Phillip and one on the jack. He slowly motioned me forward. I closed until the rabbit was fifteen feet away. I looked to Phillip. He nodded. I focused intently on the rabbit and started to draw the bow.

The rabbit hopped off a few feet under a bunch of prickly pear. Suddenly Phillip was somehow back alongside me. I started.

He whispered, "Don't focus on the rabbit. He will feel your intention. Use relaxed vision. See him."

I walked forward slowly and smoothly. I only saw the rabbit in my peripheral vision. But then luminous vision kicked in, and he was easy to see. His halo flared more yellow and brighter than the surrounding vegetation. I closed within fifteen feet of him.

"Now raise the bow but not toward him." I raised the bow but not towards the rabbit. "Now, point, relax and release," he whispered.

I turned the bow toward the jack, brought the bowstring back and the arrow to my nose, pushed the bow out and pointed with my nose and left index finger, then I sighed, exhaling and— released.

The arrow disappeared and the jack bounded off. I thought it had missed but Phillip shook his head and pointed. I followed his finger and finally I saw it. The rabbit was under the mesquite, the arrow buried deeply in its side and under its shoulder. We walked over to him. The rabbit was alive but barely. The arrow heaved up and down with his last ragged breaths.

Phillip squatted down and pulled the little buckskin pollen bag out from underneath his shirt. "See him as he dies. Watch his luminosity."

He touched his hand to the rabbit's side and left it lightly there as if checking for a pulse or letting him know that he was not alone. We squatted there in silence as the sun set and the light went out of that rabbit's eyes.

There was no cheering as I had witnessed when I had hunted cottontails back in the Ohio cornfields. No jubilation. Phillip never mentioned what I had thought was an excellent shot. In fact I don't think he ever mentioned it again. He had expected me as a man to shoot straight, just as he now expected me to sit in wake for this dying animal. It was a far cry from the many stories and movies featuring the brutal torture that the Apache were so infamous for. I wanted to bring it up, the Apache reputation for torture, but it was neither the time nor the place. I squatted in silence and watched the rabbit die.

He dipped his fingers into the little buckskin bag and withdrew it, his brown fingers covered in bright yellow pollen. Reverently he crossed the rabbit's head with pollen.

Then his hand rose straight up above the head dropping pollen dust as he did till his hand was about a foot over the rabbit's head.

Just then the rabbit twitched and died. He voided a couple of pellets as he released control of all his muscles, including his bowels.

"I didn't know I—"

"Shh," Phillip interrupted, "Keep seeing."

I turned my attention back to the rabbit. The luminosity still emanated from around the body.

Time passed. The sun dropped low in the sky. And then something happened. A small, tennis ball-sized luminous orb slowly, almost imperceptibly emerged from the corpse and slowly, almost reluctantly, drifted upward along the course of the falling pollen dust.

But it didn't stop there. It passed through Phillip's hand and continued to slowly drift upwards like a small glowing balloon. It slowly tumbled and gyrated in and upon itself, pulsing and fading—a little luminous soap bubble. Inside, deep inside was a shining sphere with tiny but brilliant white sparkles and vertical lines that constantly shifted and turned. Gradually, lazily, the orb pulsed and drifted upwards until it was high in the darkening night sky.

My mouth hung open in amazement. I watched as it continued to rise and drift as if on some unseen luminous wind, till it was as small but less bright and a little less clear than the emerging evening stars. Finally I lost it—one more star among a myriad of other stars.

I finally turned to look at Phillip. I shook my head and opened my mouth.

"Was that what I think it was?"

"Don't think. See and then know."

"That—what I saw, was the soul of the jack." Phillip stared back at me impassively. "And the pollen traced the route it took. It's the same color as the luminosity."

"So it is a good physical reference point for the luminosity," he added. "Everything we do is practical. Nothing is solely symbolic or ceremonial. But the reason for many things in the old ways has been forgotten."

I looked down at the jack rabbit. "But what was the purpose of taking the life of the rabbit? What are we going to do with it now?"

Phillip looked at me with a bemused expression. "We are going to eat him of course. The rocks are alive too, but they're much harder to digest and don't taste so good."

He drew a pocket knife, locked it out and deftly slit the rabbit's throat, hanging him upside down. The blood quickly drained out.

Next he slit the belly. Then he cut out the guts and carefully set them aside.

"That is our offering back to the mother," he said.

He worked casually but respectfully. He poked holes in the limbs and blew into the holes. The hide magically separated off the body and he carefully pulled it off. Then he began slicing off chunks of meat.

"We need a fire."

I fished in my pockets. "I didn't bring a lighter," I said sheepishly.

"Here," he handed me the bloody knife, butt first. "Cut some sticks and skin 'em to roast the meat on."

"What are you going to do?"

"Build a fire," he replied.

Phillip unslung the quiver. It was a traditional Apache quiver. It had a stick running the vertical length of it, to shape it. I had seen many in books and a few in museums. I thought it was a decorative feature. He slid the stick running the length of the quiver out and reached into the bottom of it, puling out a small concave piece of blackened wood. He put it between his feet and reached back into the quiver withdrawing a handful of fine, dry tinder.

I moved off to cut the sticks. I returned with two sharpened sticks less than ten minutes later to a small steady blaze. Phillip took the sticks and skewered two hunks of meat on them, crushing something on them as well.

"Sage, tastes good too." He placed a skewer over the fire and handed me the other. "All life lives on the death of other life, and all life is sentient. Even the rocks."

"Grass too?" I asked.

"Grass too," Phillip said.

"Guess there's no point to being a vegetarian then," I said.

"If it makes you feel better," he replied.

The sun set with its characteristic Arizona splendor. The Arizona night sky spilled out its diamond spray. The rabbit sizzled on the spit. I lay back, watched the stars, and wondered which one was the rabbit.

**"Stand straight like a warrior and face the enemy or
the game, pull and push at the same time."**

Find a clear outside view of mountains or tree foliage with a
plain background of sky.
Stand up straight but with your chin tucked.
Tongue on the roof of your mouth.
Start a good breath cycle.
Slow your breath.
Then slow your heart.
As your heartbeat slows, watch your breathing.
Using soft, unfocused, peripheral vision, see past the moun-
tainside or foliage.
See into the distance of the sky behind and beyond the moun-
tainside.
The mountain should light up with a soft, luminous glow, or if
you are skilled, click in like switching on a neon sign.
If you hunt, know that for the Apache it is not sport, but akin
to prayer. Understand that you will be taking a life and freeing a
soul.
Observe all weapon safety rules, hunting regulations, and get
trained up first.
Hunt in a sacred way.
Respectful.
Humble.
Go out hungry. That way you have need of the kill.
Bless your kill. Give thanks for it.
Then eat it.
All of it. But give some back to the earth.

FACE DANCING

Everything is born of woman.

—Second Rule

"A<small>LMOST THERE</small>," Phillip turned back as he crested the next boulder in the stream. "You okay there, gopher killer?"

"Great," I gasped. I paused to catch my breath and turned as well to look down the rock slope. We were deep into Bear Canyon late on a balmy Sunday afternoon. The Tucson city valley stretched out before us in all of its magnificent sprawl. "We going all the way to Seven Falls?"

"*Da'aa.*"

"Why not?" I asked.

"Too crowded, too many tourists. We need a secluded spot with a good reflecting pool—which if memory serves, is just up ahead."

Of course 'just up ahead' meant another two miles, but we made it. I was bone tired. Phillip didn't seem to notice much. He stepped through a stand of willows and cattails into an isolated section of the canyon stream.

The rich, gold-hued sandstone rock was smooth and comfortable from generations of water coursing through, cutting and polishing it into every imaginable shape. A shallow offshoot of the main stream flowed into a shallow pool, and then meandered on downstream as water does. On the bank a cottonwood spread long branches covered in pale green leaves creating an inviting shade. In front of the pool were two rounded sandstone outcroppings which formed natural seats.

We sat down. I passed him my canteen but he drank from the stream instead, using a hollow reed he had attached to the ever present buckskin cord around his neck.

"It's a hollowed out cattail reed for novice warriors on their manhood quest. But still it's handy for drinking from the cracks in the rocks. Settle in. Get comfortable. Sit up straight in warrior seat." I did as I was told. He sat back too.

"Circle up your spine in a clockwise motion four times, until each vertebra is sitting atop the one beneath it." I circled up. "Tuck your chin; touch your tongue to the roof of your mouth." I complied.

"Now watch your breathing slow, then your heartbeat." After a few minutes I was there. After months of practice I could drop into battle breathing quickly and even slow my heart with little trouble.

I was lost deep in my breathing cycle when I heard Phillip's warm, whiskey voice directing me. "...And when you are ready, leaving your eyes unfocused and keeping your vision in a peripheral mode, slowly open your eyes and gaze into the pool."

I opened my eyes and saw my reflection in the water, clear but a little darker than in life because of the water.

"Pick up your luminosity; tell me when you do," he said.

In moments I said, "I've got it."

"Good," Phillip intoned. "Now look past your head and shoulders as if they were a mountain range and you are looking into the valley beyond, and only with your peripheral vision see your own face..."

I watched my face in the still pool. The water was like glass. I stared into my own eyes in the pool.

"Don't blink," Phillip whispered. I watched me. My eyes stared into my eyes which stared into my eyes. Then incredibly, my face began to fade and change!

The water was still but my face melted and morphed. A dark-skinned, fierce full-blood Indian face replaced mine, then it faded and a Japanese face replaced it. I could even make out the armored samurai helmet. Then that too was gone—replaced by an old man with long white hair, then that face changed and there was a hook-nosed, bearded, auburn-haired man, then a Greek in a bronze horse-hair helmet replaced that image, then a bald-headed Tibetan in saffron robes, then a grimy and gaunt face in a World War Two U.S. soldier's helmet … and so it went, on and on in an endless litany of life in all its generations and varied societies, and not in any kind of chronological order.

My head swam and my vision blurred, but I held on and refused to blink. Finally my face disappeared altogether and only blackness remained in my head and shoulders as if some cosmic loop had run its course.

"Circle down and break the straightness of your spine, *shiyee*. That was very well done." Phillip's hand was on my shoulder.

I closed my eyes and bent my spine. My eyes were sore and swollen and I closed and rubbed them and then grabbed some water from the pool and splashed them. For good measure I took a drink.

I lay back on the warm, smooth rock face, exhausted by the intensity of my effort. I closed my eyes and let the warm afternoon sun beat down upon me. The next thing I knew Phillip was shaking me awake.

"Time for debrief," he said.

"So that wasn't a dream?" I asked. He shook his head.

"You're not getting off that easy. Now what did you see?"

"Well, I am not sure, I…" It seemed just too surreal to now say what I actually seen. I was uncertain if it had been my imagination or not, and I was reluctant to make a mistake so great, and reveal the enormity of my error.

"That," Phillip interjected, "right there is ego resurfacing. Right now. You are afraid to be wrong. Fear is ego, and leads to anger, anger leads to hate, and hate leads to closing off, disconnecting from *Ulsen* and all our relations."

He stretched his long legs out in front of him. "Did you see the Indian one? You definitely have native blood somewhere back there. Probably Apache or Comanche. But that one with the bronze helmet. I think maybe that was Spartan. I guess you'll be tough enough and stubborn enough for this road." He said it casually—almost lazily.

I was stunned and turned to him open-mouthed and dumb-founded. "But—how do you know that?"

He shook his head, plucked a piece of grass and stuck it in his mouth. "You know this is going to take a lot longer than I thought if you keep asking me the same questions every time I teach you something new."

"You mean...you saw them too?" I ran my fingers through my then brown hair.

"Why do you think I am actually telling you something this time?"

"So, that ...I'll know...they were actually there. Those faces, they're real."

The realization hit me hard in the stomach and I took a deep breath. We both sat quietly for a while, Phillip allowing the enormity of the experience to soak in to my intellect. "So we both saw them."

"Because they were, and are, really there," Phillip replied. Face dancing—this is an old way of seeing from many times, cultures and many peoples. Now to work. Where are those faces, within you or without? Don't think, just sit up straight, and put your tongue on the roof of your mouth and answer—now."

I did as I was told. I slowed my breathing and watched my heartbeat. I became quiet. Then suddenly I blurted out "Within. Because they are all a part of me—an aspect of my soul at various times and...."

"In Ndee we call this *nohwiza ye bi kigoyaii*. Ancestor wisdom: the wisdom contained in the energies of places and the probabilities of these places, as in courses of probabilities."

"Like the paths of electrons and neutrons?" I asked. Phillip nodded.

"So you are saying that they not only are who I was, but who I could have been. Because we don't know the precise orbits of electrons and such, we just sort of guess at their probable course based upon their characteristics."

"*Tuu* is a perfect illustration of your dilemma."

"*Tuu?*"

"'Water' in Ndee." Phillip dipped his hand in the water. "Where is this water now?"

"Here," I said, "that's the easiest one you've ever asked me."

"What about that water there?" He pointed downstream.

"Downstream, of course," I answered easily.

"What about that *tuu* there?" He indicated upstream.

"Upstream obviously." I smiled.

"Show me the line."

"What line?"

"The line delineating the upstream water from the midstream from the downstream." He dipped his fingers and then flicked a droplet back into the stream. "Is that droplet down or midstream now?" He looked at me. Once again I was stumped and he knew it. I squinted back at him.

"A true, whole man must be competent physically and spiritually. That means he is able to comprehend realities of all types, physical and spiritual, and function in whatever realm he is called to serve. For instance, tell me gopher, how does time flow?"

"Past, present, future." This time I omitted the "easy" remarks. I was no longer sure of anything.

"Where are we now?"

"Well...here, of course; why?" He got up and ambled upstream, motioning me to follow him. I did, of course, although I was quite stiff now from the earlier climb. He stopped about thirty yards up. "Where are we now?"

"Thirty yards or so upstream, why?"

"So tell me again how time flows. Don't think. Just stand up straight and answer."

It hit me in a rush. "We are here now but we were there," I indicated downstream, "Time flows present to past."

"Or ..." He looked at me.

"Or ...present to future. But it's always flowing."

"Like time. But who determines where we stand at the stream?"

"We do."

"Stay there." He walked ten yards upstream from me. "Who is upstream?"

"You are."

He walked downstream. "And now?"

"I am. Are you saying that we determine where we are in time and space based upon where we focus our attention?"

He grinned. "No, but you just did. Come on."

He hiked along the stream until we came to a small waterfall. The spray misted his face and his brown beaver-felt cowboy hat. He leaned back and sat back down on a rock. I copied him and stuck my head in the mist as well. It felt great. I stuck my tongue out.

"You know this mist is still water."

"I know."

"Some winters, it even snows and this stream freezes—of course it's all still H_2O. Right?"

"Right." I was desperately trying to catch up, but wasn't sure where I was heading.

"And you know, sometimes that heron over there," he nodded at a huge blue heron on the far side of the bank sunning its wings that I had somehow completely missed, "sometimes that heron drinks some of this stream, but...." He looked at me.

"It's still water...so whether it's frozen or liquid or mist or even heron pee, it's all still water. You're talking about energy and how it can't be destroyed."

I thought for a moment, then realized I was thinking and tried to stop. Suddenly I blurted out, "And reincarnation. You're also talking about reincarnation. And how time flows and space folds, aren't you?" I was once again on track and amazed.

"Guess that depends on what level of meaning you take my words at, doesn't it?"

"Uh," I was lost again.

"All things are alive to those that have eyes to see and ears to hear. And nothing and nobody is created equal.

"But," he held up a brown, long index finger, "we can all be delineated by our different and varying level of sentience, of self-awareness. So a simpler boy than you might have only understood I was talking about birds and water. All things are alive—even the rocks. The difference is their level of self-awareness."

He kept walking. "Even the grass screams when you cut it."

"Hey, you just told me something. I thought you didn't do that."

"That? That's common scientific knowledge. Got that from Mr. Falcon at the U of A's Earth Sciences department." He shrugged. "I said I would not tell you how or what to think about, what do you call it—Bob?"

"Ah, yes, Bob...I almost forgot," I said. "Maybe Bob is sentience itself."

"Maybe, maybe not. Or maybe the Hare Krishnas are right. I don't like maybes. I like knowing, and as long as you are my apprentice, I expect you to do so as well."

"I'm your apprentice?" I asked.

"Of course you are. That's what the traditional gift was for."

"Gift, what gift?"

"The *keiban*. You paid for and brought me the *keiban* remember?" He stopped walking and stared at me. "You didn't think we'd start this ceremony improperly, do you?"

"No, course not." We started walking, "What ceremony?"

Phillip actually started laughing. Not in a sarcastic or spiteful way. Just good plain laughter. He stopped and turned to me. "This ceremony. Us. Me training you. This is a ceremony. Of all the ceremonies I've performed in my life, this is probably the most important. So you'd better earn this opportunity. No pressure though."

He looked at my ashen face and started laughing again. "Don't worry, this is the easy part. "Later on it will be much, much harder."

"What will?"

"Whatever it is you will have to do with the training I give to you."

"Why don't you do it?"

"I can't do it. Besides, I've done more than my share. Before I started, there were no *Na'ii'ees* on the reservation. Until now it was against the law for Indians to practice their religion. Now there are several *diyin* performing *Na'ii'ees* besides me. Our sunrise ceremony has brought a new dawn for the Apache. My people are reviving and returning."

"And, what was the point of the gift again?"

"To ask, of course. You have to ask for this, of your own free will."

He stopped walking and turned to face me full on. "You do remember asking, right?" I nodded numbly, desperately trying to remember asking.

"Because that would be pretty funny, you forgetting that you asked for all this trouble." He laughed again.

"You're not exactly a reassuring figure. I mean, I never hear you talk about achieving world peace through enlightenment—or stuff like that."

Phillip stared at me for a long moment. His smile spread. His white teeth gleamed against his brown, wrinkled face. His eyes creased into small slits. Then he was shaking, guffawing and cackling. He stumbled on the smooth river rock and almost fell, but recovered, still laughing.

"World peace! That's a good one, I gotta remember that one." He stumbled on down the river bank still laughing. "We just had to fight the entire United States Army, dragging our women and kids with us."

He kept laughing as he rounded the bend and went out of sight. I just stood there, wondering how come I wasn't laughing.

"A true, whole man must be competent physically and spiritually."

Back to your folded blanket, sage stick, and matches again.
But add a mirror.
Place it so you can see your head and shoulders in it when seated.
Dim the light and ensure the light source is not just on one side of your face.
Sit again in man seat.
Circle up your spine in a clockwise motion four times, until each vertebra is sitting atop the one beneath it.
Tuck your chin.
Touch your tongue to the roof of your mouth.
Watch your breathing slow.
Then slow your heartbeat.
Now just watch your breathing.
And when you are ready, leaving your eyes unfocused and keeping your vision in a peripheral mode, slowly open your eyes and gaze into the mirror.
Pick up your luminosity around your head and shoulders.
Now look past your head and shoulders as if they were a mountain range and you are looking into the valley beyond, and only with your peripheral vision see your own face.
Don't blink.
Your face should begin to fade and change!
If you see a malevolent face, or a face that looks back at you, STOP. Circle down and break the straightness of your spine.
Smudge.
Sweat.
Be very careful not to abuse this exercise.
Recall that everything herein is to be used exclusively in selfless service to others.

CHILDREN BORN
OF WAR

*And the dragon was wroth with the Lady and went to make war
upon the remnant of her seed.*
—Revelations 12:17

I PULLED INTO DAWN STAR TRADERS on Campbell next to a battered
blue, Ford pick-up truck with a bumper sticker on the back that
read "INDIANS HAD BAD IMMIGRATION LAWS TOO." I got out and entered.

Inside, Phillip was talking with two other Indian men a bit
younger than himself. Nearby two non-Indian, middle-aged ladies, heavily bedecked in expensive Navajo jewelry, were busily
setting up a table with books on it.

I walked up and nodded. They ignored me for a while and
finished their conversation. I glanced at the books on the table.
The titles read: *God Is Red,* and *Custer Died for Your Sins.* Then
Phillip introduced me all around.

"This is Vine Deloria and Harlyn Gokliya."

"Sir, I met you at the University of Dayton a couple of years
back," I said to Deloria, "I've read your books there." I nodded at
the table. Deloria nodded gravely.

"Doing a book signing here today," Deloria replied.

"Are you teaching at the U of A now?" I asked.

"Treaty law." Deloria was a brilliant Lakota lawyer and author
I had first met at the University of Dayton at a film highlighting
the Shoshone nation's legal fight for their homelands. Now I was

bumping back into him in Tucson. He was the first Native American attorney to pull out all the treaties that the government of the United States had made with the various Indian nations, then broken, and haul them into their own courts.

The other man I didn't recognize at first, but then it hit me, "Gokliya?"

The wide, thin mouth, high cheekbones, hawk nose and flint eyes were unmistakable. I had seen them hundred times in dozens of old photographs.

"The great grandson of Geronimo?"

Gokliya nodded even more gravely. Now that I was aware of it, the resemblance was uncanny.

Neither shook my hand. I could sense but not understand that my status had changed. Phillip was not his normal jovial self either.

"So," Phillip said, "your spiritual childhood is over. Your first cycle of purification was to return you to an open, innocence of childhood, so that you'd experience the luminous world. And you have. You have seen the luminescent radiance of all folks and things, you have seen the spiritual aspect within your own soul, and you have even seen the soul of the rabbit when it left at death."

He grabbed a blanket off a nearby table and spread it on the floor. It was a Pendleton which displayed a circle quartered in four colors: red, yellow, black and white. Beyond the globe the blanket itself was quartered in these same four colors but in reverse.

"So now you know, because you have seen the spiritual realm. The world is not just physical. There is a world of faith—of things unseen visible only to those with eyes to see."

The ladies had stopped working and were listening respectfully as well. Phillip was always a commanding presence in his own right. But the air created by the three of these men together was impossible to ignore. It made me wonder what it must have been like to be in a traditional native council with a company of such men gathered in one lodge.

"If you were a physical child, we would hold a First Step ceremony for you. We'd have you walk in the four directions on this blanket east to north. Your mom would make pollen footprints with the bottom of her fist and toe prints with her little finger—just like White Painted Lady did to fool the Dragon when he came to devour her child." Phillip paused.

"She hid *Tubadish'd'ne'e* under the fire and fooled the Dragon, after all the people drowned in the flood," Golkiya added. "But *Nayae'skane'e* still had to slay the Dragon."

"Somebody always has to," Phillip chuckled.

"*Nayeskane'e,* I know, is Slayer of Monsters, but *Tuba* is?"

"Child Born of Water," Phillip said quietly.

The doors of the store opened and customers began filtering in and heading directly towards the book table. Deloria nodded to Phillip and Gokliya, and moved off to his table and the gathering crowd.

"Your mother would push you off in these four directions and I would entice you forward with an *itsa'a,* an eagle feather. So in that way you would own the cycles of your life."

"Cycles?" I interrupted.

"All life is cyclical. Spring, summer, fall and winter. Childhood, boyhood, manhood, old age. These last couple of months you have completed your spiritual childhood. But you are a physically grown man. So your ceremony will be a little different."

"Pick you up Saturday morning at six AM at Phillip's," Gokliya said tersely to me and then turned to Phillip.

Gokliya shook Phillip's hand and headed towards the door. He turned at the door and looked back at me, "And be ready to run." He walked out.

"Run?" I looked back to Phillip.

"Now you know that it's not just who dies with the most toys wins, that there is a spiritual aspect to the world, and a spiritual essence to yourself. You have experienced *diyi*—power through all your senses: touch, hearing, smell—which is also taste, but especially sight, because we are primarily sighted beings. Now you know. Because you have seen. And seeing is believing. Now that you know that there is something beyond the grave, you know that there is something worth fighting for, worth dying for, worth killing for, worth sacrificing for. Now it is time for you in your youth cycle to strengthen and empower yourself physically and spiritually."

"Why physically? I'm in great shape."

Phillip smiled only slightly at my question. "When you do access luminous power, it will charge you with current and your physical body must be ready to keep up."

"Start doing pushups and sit-ups and stretching. Eat plenty of meat and protein. You're plenty lean after your purification; now you're going to be all muscle. And stop by Steve's. Get some hi-tops made." He smiled. You're goin' to need 'em. Now get going."

I got going. It was Saturday so I went straight to Steve's. And he was there.

I ordered the moccasins. Steve was ecstatic. Especially when I said I needed them by next Saturday, since a rush order was an extra seventy-five bucks. With the deal sealed he got a little curious.

"What's the hurry?"

"Phillip wants me to have them for some kind of run next Saturday," I replied.

"Some kind of protest-prayer run going on that I haven't heard about?" Steve wondered. He put a piece of paper on the ground as we talked.

"What's a protest run?" I asked.

"Put one foot on that. Well, when most groups want to protest something, they hold a sit-in or a rally or whatever and get a bunch of news coverage of them chanting or waving signs or burning flags. But that's not the way the Apache do it. Like with the Mount Graham thing."

"What's the Mount Graham thing?" I bit.

"Apaches claim, especially Phillip's one sister Sara, the political activist, that Mount Graham is a sacred place to them. The U of A and the Vatican are trying to build a telescope there—and the Apaches are against it." Steve bent down and traced the outline of my foot with a marker on the paper.

"And that has what to do with Apache running?" I was even getting lost talking to Steve.

"Oh, sorry; well the Apaches don't have the hang of the protest thing. You know they're all about being the strong, silent type people. So instead of holding up signs and calling channel four, they do a protest run." Now he took a tape measure to my calf and knee.

"Like I said before, what's a protest run?" I looked down at Steve.

"Well, they'll run from Graham to Tucson—something like a couple hundred miles, carrying like an eagle feather or something. They think it's like praying or something. And nobody on the news wants to cover a several hundred mile run with some crazy Indians, so they never make the six o'clock news. They just don't get it. What color uppers?" We walked to a table near the back of the store. On it sat variants of all of Steve's moccasin types. I chose a nice buff color, closest to the color of Phillip's.

"Don't get what?" I asked.

"The noble red man prayer thing. It doesn't sell. Sex and violence. Big time wrestling. Train wrecks. Screaming protestors. Burning flags. Those sell. But running down a mountain side in the rain—they just don't get it. That's why they're stuck on those reservation ghettos."

"You're right," I said heading for the door, "they just don't get it."

"Come back Friday," Steve called after me.

I did, and lo and behold the moccasins were ready. But they weren't exact duplicates in the Apache style. They lacked a turned up toe piece and no ties to firm them up around the ankles. The seam went across the instep instead of just up the sides.

"These are better and they'll last longer. These uppers are buffalo. Much better than the crap they make up on the reservation—if you can even get them. It's a lost art up there."

I had to admit they were beautiful in their own right. The rawhide sole was flat, thick and creamy white. It was contoured up around the toes and side of the feet to provide solid protection from cactus thorns and sharp rocks. The upper hides were near an eighth of an inch thick. I doubted even the thickest cactus spine would penetrate them.

"They're beautiful," I admitted. "You did a great job." I paid the full price and the extra seventy-five happily.

In the years to come Steve would build quite a reputation for himself building moccasins. He would even become the source for all of my students throughout the world and the film industry as well. He provided authentic Apache footwear and other items for such films as *Geronimo* and *The Missing*. Steve talked tough but that was about it. Underneath it all he had a kind heart. I started to leave. But Steve stopped me.

"Put 'em on. Make sure they fit." I did and they did. Like a leather foot glove.

"They're the most comfortable things I have ever worn."

"Yeah," Steve laughed, "I get that a lot."

"No, I mean it, they feel amazing!" I preened in front of the low shoe mirror Steve had propped up at floor height.

"I feel like Laurence of Arabia." I headed out to my car and took off still wearing them. I almost slept in them that night.

Saturday morning I was at Phillip's bright, early and on time. Gokliya was waiting outside, squatting on the doorstep sipping a cup of coffee. He got in without a word.

"Morning," I said, "how are you, sir?"

"Head east out to Catalina Highway and up towards Mount Lemon," he replied.

"So what are we doing ?"

"You're running. I'm driving."

"Where am I running and you driving?"

"Up," he pointed with his chin, "there." Mount Lemon rose massively before us. The Catalina highway zigzagged up it till it wound around out of sight.

"Why?" I was getting exasperated.

"Because he asked me and told you."

"Looks like a long way. How far am I going?"

"Till you run into me."

He pulled off at the picnic area just as the road started to rise onto the mountain. I looked over at him. He looked at me

"Any advice?"

He was silent for a long while. I opened my door to get out.

"You want to learn Apache traditional ways, then you got to learn how to run. We are great runners. My grandpa, he outran the cavalry horses. He and his men could cover seventy-five miles at the trot in a day, over rocky terrain that would break a horse's leg the first quarter mile. They'd steal a horse right out of the rancher's corral, under his nose, then they'd ride till it couldn't go any further, then build a fire under it, to get it up, ride it till it died, eat some, make a canteen out of some of the stomach, then run on foot till they stole more."

He put the truck in park but kept staring straight ahead, I looked at him.

"You gonna run or stand there all day?"

In answer I hopped out of the truck and slammed the door. I nodded to him.

"*Ahie'e.*" I said trying out my Nde'e. I turned uphill and took a long stride. The slick new rawhide slid smartly on the sand and pine needles and I went face forward on the hot, black pavement.

I caught myself on my palms, but my right knee scraped along the rugged road. I stood up quickly, totally embarrassed, and looked quickly at Harlyn.

He was laughing quietly and definitely at me. The kindness of Phillip's amusement was totally absent. Like his great grandfather, this was a hard man.

I looked at my knee. It was a bloody scrape with gravel stuck here and there. I went to brush out the pebbles with my palm and saw that my palm was a bloody smear as well, with pebbles of its own. I carefully picked the pebbles out of each palm with the opposite hand, then removed them from my knee. Everything stung like acid.

"Want to go home to your fancy sports car and Jacuzzi?" he called out from the cab.

"How'd you know about the Jacuzzi?"

"All you college boys got 'em. Come on, I'll take you back home. Playin' Indian gettin' hard, huh?"

With conscious effort I shut my mouth and turned away. I started running carefully up the mountain road. The rawhide soles were like running on ice. And, unlike a running shoe, there was no cushion in the hard rawhide. I could feel every sharp pebble push against the unyielding iron surface of the asphalt. Plus the soles were stiff with newness and did not bend much with my foot.

The first half mile I tried to strike with my heels but the impact was already bruising them. I set my mouth in a tight line and tried to stay with the heel strike, but in the next instant the slick rawhide sole sent my left leg out in front of me and the rawhide tip of my right toe caught on something.

I did an unintentional split way too fast and way too hard. In the process I managed to scrape off whatever remaining unskinned area there was while taking off a fresh level from the already bloody section.

I pulled my legs together. I had definitely pulled a muscle in my upper thigh, maybe my groin. Both burned. So did my palms. I examined my wounds. At least there were no pebbles to pull out this time.

"Damn it!" Just then Harlyn pulled up. He wasn't laughing this time, but he did shake his head.

"You ain't gonna make it, *Ligai*," he called out to me. "You come get in this truck now. I'll take you to the emergency room."

"Maybe the morgue. But not now, not yet." Slowly I started to heave myself up to my feet. As I moved, pain shot through my body and anger followed white hot. Without looking over at him I yelled, "You don't think I'm tough enough to do this Apache shit. Got news for you. I'm American. And in case you forgot, your great grandpa surrendered to the Americans! So that makes us Americans the toughest warriors. And I am running this mountain. So just shut up and leave me alone!"

I heard the truck engine cut and the door open. I looked over and could hardly believe my eyes. My stomach dropped and my adrenaline dumped. Geronimo was striding towards me—with a large fixed blade bowie knife in one hand! I tried to rise but he was on me too quickly. He bent down toward me and I kicked out at him. He caught my leg under the ankle with his free hand.

"Hold still now. Stop kicking like Crook's mules." He was cutting at the bottoms of the soles of my moccasins.

"What the hell are you doing?"

"Give me the other one," he commanded.

Amazingly I did. He started cutting on that one as well.

"Scoring the soles for traction. Take a look." He dropped my foot. I crossed my leg and put the foot up to look at the sole. True to his word Harlyn had scored the rawhide perpendicular to the length.

"Flex your foot."

I did and watched the cuts open up like a snake's belly scales.

"Works like snakeskin for traction." It was as if he had read my mind.

"But I have to run on the balls of feet to open the scoring," I complained.

"Yeah, *Ligai*, that's how you run in *keiban*. This is the desert. You run out here in your little cushioned, nylon Nikes and you'll get a barrel hook thorn up your foot a couple of inches. Then you'll know real pain. Those things flatten tires. How do you think we ran hundreds of miles without your fancy padded shoes? We run like wolves run. A steady trot. But like all our four-legged relations, on the balls of our feet. No four-legged runner runs on their heel—because they don't have heels!" We stared at each other for a long moment.

I turned away and trotted off, desperately trying to figure out how to run in these things. "Please, God," I whispered, "don't let me fall again."

I took off running gingerly. I kept my strikes light and short. And now I did not extend my stride at all but kept my feet under my torso. That increased my stability.

"Course I'll probably get passed by a land tortoise at this pace," I muttered under my breath.

Next I got off the pavement. That was a huge improvement. The bare ground gave way and the sharp little pebbles and rocks sunk into the ground with each foot strike, so that I did not feel them anymore.

I also discovered that while the moccasins were terrible on artificial surfaces like the road, they were ideal on the natural ones that they were designed for. I did not sink in the sandy places because of the flatness of the sole, but kind of glided on it.

Since I was no longer over-extending my stride, it was easy now to strike on the balls of my feet. The soles flexed open and grabbed the irregular ground, and the balls of my feet provided a natural spring to my stride.

"I might just live through this," I muttered.

The next couple of miles I spent refining my new running technique. It was definitely easier and more natural and took any slamming impact off my neck and spine, since the heel bone was no longer involved in the stride.

As the road steepened, I found I needed to lean forward more, and that, I found, took even more stress and strain off my spine. Next I took inventory of the rest of me. I realized my hands were clenched and creating additional tension. I inhaled deeply and let go of the tension in my hands and arms, letting them drop and hang. My chest immediately loosened and I found I could breathe deeper.

Breathing—of course! I remembered Phillip's battle breath and started a proper breath cycle. That helped immensely. I fell into a rhythm of breathing and running.

By the time I had myself together, I looked up and I was among the tall Ponderosa pines. It was noticeably cooler. My palms and knee still stung with each breeze, but they were starting to congeal so I felt it less. I must have covered several miles. I looked back for Harlyn but he was nowhere to be seen.

I covered more miles. The desert floor spilled out below me now far below. I passed Windy Point and got some weird looks from the tourists. A couple actually snapped photos of my feet. I jogged by a popular grove. I started passing beautiful pull-off vistas. Then I got thirsty. And tired and stiff and sore. I looked around for Harlyn. I trotted on.

My legs became like iron. My knees and palm throbbed and swelled. I was stiff with thirst, lactic acid and just plain exhaustion. The sun burned me and the wind seared the burn. I had no hat and the rising sun pounded my forehead. My skull throbbed with the pain of dehydration. I squinted into the brilliant sunshine and that too added to my headache. My mouth was completely dry. My lips were swollen. I was light-headed and my vision began to tunnel and go gray. I stopped sweating and even started to feel cool. Vaguely I realized I was heading towards heat stroke.

My vision narrowed to a section of roadside just ahead of me. The skin on my shoulders and neck sizzled. My head pounded. I shambled along, the moccasins thudding softly in the dust. My world narrowed to the simplicity of a single step. Then another, then another. There was nothing else. Nothing to the side. Nothing above or below, just the little circular patch of roadside ahead of me. And the next toe strike, and the next.

Then I was not even touching the ground anymore. I was just gliding. Just riding a line pulled from the center of my soul. My eyes were slits. I no longer felt anything. I barely could even see. The patch of ground in front of me was small and circular and gray. I just glided, pulled along from my center.

I lost time and space. I just ran or rather glided. In between the glide the balls of my feet briefly and just barely brushed the earth. My heart lulled itself into a slow rhythm. Alone in the universe beyond space and time, I ran on, suspended beyond perception.

"Hey, in here, here!"

Harlyn's voice echoed in my head and swam towards me through a sea of gray fog. I blinked.

The world clicked back into focus. I turned my head with a great, long effort. I had passed him and his truck. I did a long, slow turn, like an airplane banking, and headed back towards him.

I vaguely saw Gokliya pointing me on, towards something ahead, something glittering and shining in the sunshine. Nearly blind from heat stroke and exhaustion I ran on. That's all I knew how to do now. My universe was simple. One foot in front of the other—forever.

I fell abruptly face forward into the lake and went under. The shock of the cold liquid jolted through me like an electric current and I opened my mouth. The waters engulfed me. I swallowed so much I thought I'd drown. Then I got my feet under me and stood up. I broke the surface.

I swayed, unsteady on my feet and slipped in the bottom muck, going back under before I could catch myself.

I got my feet back under me with great effort. I was very tired and any movement took a great, concentrated effort. I rose up slowly dripping and shaking, as much from exhaustion as the freezing water. The first thing I saw was Gokliya who was of course laughing hysterically. I started to wade to shore but as I did, he called out to me.

"You stay there."

"Why?" I said with a mouthful of water.

"Cause I said so."

"That ain't good enough." I started back to shore.

"My great grandpa used to train our *Bedonkohe* novice boys just like this. Make 'em run up the mountain to greet the sunrise, and then jump in those mountain streams. Then he'd make 'em stand in there for a long time, to toughen 'em up."

"Yeah, well you ain't Geronimo, and I ain't an Apache novice." I was done and my patience was at an end.

I had my head down and was trudging through the shallows when something hard struck me sharply in the solar plexus. I tumbled back into the water yet again with a resounding splash.

I surfaced with what little energy I had left. I didn't know how many miles I had run up that mountain that day—probably about ten, but it felt like twenty-five. I was done.

Gokliya was laughing even harder if that was possible and he had a long stick in his hands, presumably the same stick he had just jabbed in my gut. I started to speak and realized he had knocked some of the wind out of me.

"He used to keep the boys in there for hours till the sunrise—with this stick. How you likin' old time Apache training?" He laughed.

"Not a frigging bit," I muttered as I waded ashore.

Gokliya went to jab me again, but this time I caught the stick in both hands, and pushed it back into his chest, but he held on. I jerked backwards with all my might and he tumbled headfirst into the water. He released his grip then on the stick and I whipped it back over my head.

His head exploded out of the lake and he stood up glaring at me. I must have got a good arc on that stick because he and I stared at each other a long while before I heard it finally splash.

I smiled. His eyes could have melted lead. As I waded ashore, Gokliya splashed out ahead of me and headed back up the sandy slope. Through the pines I could make him out at his pick-up. I got to shore and fell more than sat down.

A rolled-up newspaper plopped at my feet. "Pick it up and stand up!" he barked.

"What the hell are you talking about?" I looked up. Gokliya stood over me with an identical rolled-up paper in his right hand. With his left he beckoned to me in an unmistakable gesture of combat.

His answer was again a terse beckoning of his hand. I shook my head.

"All right, I get it." I lunged upwards at him with my paper.

My body was frozen, numb and exhausted. My movement was slow and clumsy. Gokliya easily clubbed me down with his newspaper. My forehead thumped the ground and slapped the earth in frustration.

Gokliya's boots appeared in front of me. I sighed.

"I—am tired—of this—SHIT!" I yelled and spun around from my hands and knees. I hooked Gokliya's right leg from behind with my left foot while simultaneously striking the front of his leg with my right.

Gokliya went down hard on his ass and I leaped onto him to stab him with my paper. But he was too quick and got his legs up and cocked over his prone form and between my body. Before I knew what had happened, he had thrown me with his legs over his head.

I tumbled, rolled, then staggered to my feet. Gokliya was on me in a flash, stabbing me in the heart, slicing at my throat and finally executing some kind of turn which swept both my feet out from under me. I landed hard on my ass just as Gokliya's paper smashed into my nose spraying blood everywhere.

I fell back totally spent. I was simply out of energy and could not move anymore. I looked up at the clouds lazily drifting across the sky through the giant Ponderosa pines. I could taste the metallic tinge of blood in my mouth from my nose. I thought about wiping it but decided it took too much effort. I spit half-heartedly, but it just sprayed back on my face.

In the distance I heard the pick-up's door slam and the engine cough to life. Gravel crunched and the motor's growl faded into the distance. I raised my head. The pick-up was gone in a trail of dust.

"Great," I said to myself, "now I get to walk home." My eyes closed and I went mercifully into a deep sleep.

"I might just live through this."

Get off the pavement.

Go for a run on bare ground.

You may not have mocs, but there are now running shoes that mimic running barefoot.

Get some.

Strike on the balls of the feet, or the outside edge of the heels rolling in and onto the balls.

Find a natural spring to your stride.

Remember, predators run on their pads, prey on their hooves, but nothing runs on heels—mostly because they don't have heels.

Phillip's running technique should quickly remove the slamming impact from your neck and spine since the heel bone is no longer involved in the stride.

With the stress off your spine, take inventory of the rest of you. Unclench your hands and arms. Inhale deeply through the nose, pause, and exhale via the mouth.

Let go of the tension in your hands and arms, letting them drop and hang. Expand your chest as you breathe deeply.

Start a proper breath cycle.

Fall into a rhythm of breathing and running.

Go until you are gone. You'll know you were gone because you'll notice that you're back. You shouldn't feel tired, but elated. This isn't just exercise.

It's prayer.

EMPOWERMENT

Power radiates from the fingers of my hand,
like rays from the sun.

—Silas John

"You look like road kill." Phillip's smooth, clear voice warmed me into wakefulness. I opened my eyes and there he was. The sun was just behind him, silhouetting him in gold as it set. My anger was muted by sleep, and Phillip's voice dissipated it instantly and effortlessly.

His big brown hand appeared in front of me. I took it, of course, and he pulled me to my feet. He was always pulling me to my feet, to stand on my own.

"Let's go." He turned towards Gokliya's truck. I started to follow him and stopped. He looked back. Then he shook his head in the negative. "He's not here. Come on." He turned away and continued to walk, and after a moment, I followed.

My body was stiff and sore all over. My knees, palms and face crackled with dried blood. White salt stained my shirt. My hair was matted and my clothes wrinkled.

I limped like an old man over to the passenger side of the truck. Phillip was sitting in the passenger seat looking straight ahead. I smiled and ambled slowly over to the driver side and got in.

"When do I get a break?"

"Boys get breaks, men keep working at their duties," Phillip said.

I got in and slammed the door shut. I sat there with both hands on the steering wheel. I took a deep breath.

111

"You sure about this? I may just run us off and over the side."

"If you can't get us down this mountain, you sure aren't the man for the job," he said looking over at me and smiling ever so slightly, "are you?"

I shook my head, started the engine and put it in gear. He had me again. I even smiled. His effect on me was always amazingly cathartic.

We drove in silence for quite a while. At first I was worried about going over the edge but after a while I got into the groove of driving.

"So he tell you what happened?" I looked over at him. Phillip nodded.

"What are you going to do about it?" I asked.

"I'm doin' it."

I was silent for a while. Then finally I blurted, "He's an asshole."

More silence. "I said, he's an asshole."

"Heard you the first time." He was silent again for a while.

"What you tried to do today," he said slowly, "is what twelve-year-old Apache boys did regularly in the old times. But it was hard for you, wasn't it? Because it was a new way of life."

He was quiet, but then he continued. "You got any idea what he's lived through?"

He turned towards me. "Got any idea what it's like having a great grandfather as a prisoner of war, a mass murderer and a drunk to whites, yet a patriot to Apaches? Did your parents live in a concentration camp on their own land as a conquered nation? Have you got any idea how hard it is for an Apache to compete in the white world and yet live in the Apache? How do think it feels to have the pressure of the lineage of Geronimo in an age that has absolutely no value for the ways of warriorship?"

"Do you know what year the American Indian Religious Freedom Act was passed?"

I shook my head.

"This year," he answered. "1978."

More silence for more miles. I was still trying to grasp the stunning reality that in the land of the free, founded on the principal of religious freedom for all, the freest and wildest of all people had been denied the most basic human rights—until this year. Phillip was right. I had absolutely no idea what Harlyn's life was like.

"Now," he said, "you ready to stop feeling sorry for yourself like a spoiled boy, and start enduring like a man?"

"Yes, sir. Is that why you were waiting for me this year, because the law got passed and it's legal to teach me?"

"Who happened to conquer the Apaches of the ancient world?"

"Who, the Spartans?"

"Yup."

"Well they were Greeks and they were eventually conquered by...the Romans."

"And after the Romans conquered them, what happened to Greek religion and culture?"

"Well, eventually, the Romans adopted the gods and the art and culture of the Greeks."

"So after physically conquering the Greeks, were the Romans subsequently spiritually conquered by the Greeks in turn?" I thought about that one for a while and then slowly nodded.

"Yes, I guess so."

"In fact isn't all of classical Roman culture based on the earlier Greek?"

"Yes, sir."

"Now let's switch to the modern Roman empire—America. When Europe and America were in famine, where did the answer come from, where did the lowly potato originate, the vegetable that saved the Western world from mass starvation and extinction?"

"Ireland."

"EEH!" He made a sound like a quiz show buzzer. I smiled.

"Nope. South American Indians. And what about the silver to stabilize the economy and make modern coinage possible and operable?"

"Indians?" I asked hopefully.

"Bing! Right, Potosi mine in Bolivia. Now that we're not starving and broke, let's talk about rights. Where do you think America got the idea about an individual, divine, God-given right to freedom, life, liberty and the pursuit of happiness—and that no-one has the right to tell another how to live or what to do?"

"England?"

"The English have always been subjects, not citizens. They have no tradition of freedom to bear arms as individual warriors and free men. They simply have a benevolent tyrant. Your forefathers came here to get away from England."

"The Greeks?"

"Do Americans have more in common with Greeks or American Indians? Benjamin Franklin got the idea to unite the colonies—when he broke one arrow over his knee, my Ndee name by the way, and then failed to break a bundle, thus illustrating the essential element that led to the founding of the greatest country the world has ever known—the United States of America."

"Benjamin Franklin was the first Indian agent; he saw Tecumseh do the same thing at the great Iroquois Confederacy of the Council of the Seven Nations." This one I knew.

"Cochise tried to do the same thing out here among us. He broke the arrow to institute the treaty after the Apache wars here. So did Mangas. But we were too used to our individual freedoms. But," he looked over at me, "if Cochise and Tecumseh had succeeded, your people would still be fighting inland from the coasts."

He crossed his legs. "Now let's talk about the heart of the matter. The heart of a people is their soul and, as you have literally seen now, that soul is luminously connected to the land they live on."

"That's why the Indians fought to the death for their lands! They were luminously connected to them!" A door was starting to open for me.

"We are still luminously connected to our land—nothing, not even our recent near extinction at the hands of the U.S. Government, will ever change that."

He was silent for a while again. I was excited again that I was beginning to luminously understand why people did things. It was a totally alien but natural, spiritual perspective that made absolute sense.

"And don't think I'm whining. Babies whine. Men endure. Life is never fair. We took and held this land through force. I simply don't want you whining because you got a little bruised."

"A little, what do you call that?" I pointed at my nose.

"That is nothing. Our training is stern and stoic. I'm speaking of your ego. That is the problem with kids today. They want respect in their gangs but they don't want to give any. They have not been taught to endure insult and hardship for their duty to others. They mistake cruelty for bravery. That's what gangs are anyway, shallow mimics of traditional warrior and manhood societies. The beating-in to the gang duplicates exactly the gauntlet of the Eastern nations."

"Yeah, just like with Pocahontas and John Smith," I chimed in.

"That was a Potawatomi manhood gauntlet. Smith had to prove that he could endure hardship as a man, because manhood is all about enduring the rigors of life, for the betterment of our women and children. After which came a claiming ceremony." Phillip threw up his hands.

"They weren't actually going to kill him. It was just that some woman of the tribe had to claim him, say that she had a connection to him, and thus he an obligation to her, that he was of value inside their hoop of *shitake'e*. Because remember, in a traditional society we are defined by our duties to others. If we have no obligation to anyone, then we have no duty, then we have no utility."

"And we are *yudashti'n*, born outside, a bastard like me," I said bitterly.

"There you go feeling sorry for yourself again," he sighed. "If you're still outside, who are the parents paying for your college, and why am I training you? You were born outside, but you have been blessed and welcomed into many circles."

He was right. I just didn't know how to let go of my own anger and bitterness. "How do I do it, let go of my anger and ego?"

"That is the most important question you have ever asked." He put his hand on my shoulder. It ached and was tender to the touch. I tried not to wince. "Pull off here." I pulled off at Windy

Point, the most scenic view on Mount Lemon. He got out and motioned me to follow.

He went over to the edge of the wall separating us from a thousand-foot sheer drop-off. The sun was setting, filling the sky with unimaginable shades of gold, orange, yellow, red and even green.

"This is the time for battle breath. To battle yourself, your ego, your own anger. Breathe in deeply through the nose, pause, hold, then slowly out through your mouth—letting go of the tension in your body and your heart."

I inhaled strongly, holding it until I felt I was about to pass out, and then released the air out my mouth. The breath gushed out in a long, low sigh. I felt the tension in my emotions leave as well.

"Again," Phillip ordered. I repeated the procedure and again felt physically better, even physically lighter. "Again," he said. I complied.

"Once more," he said. By then I was even smiling through my cracked lips. It was true, I felt great!

"Did you know that there is a secretion in the brain that poisons the body when you are hateful and angry?" He turned me by my shoulders to look at him. "Believe me, son, I know more about hate and anger and injustice than you ever will. But as a free man I choose not to be controlled and enslaved by anyone in any way—least of all by some petty tyrant's psychosis. The real question is—are you?"

"No, grandfather." I was now nearly moved to tears by the profundity of Phillip's concern for me and the elegance of his lesson. Looking in his face, I could see the truth of his words written in the lines of his face. But, they were laugh lines. "Thank you."

"U'gash." He hopped back into the truck and I followed, pausing momentarily that somehow, a spring had returned to my step. My stiffness began to melt away. I got in and we got underway.

"Now back to work. Where was I? Oh yeah, physical conquest and spiritual assimilation. At the end of days for the Indians there was a Paiute prophet named Wovoka. He had a dream with Jesus. And Jesus, he taught Wovoka a dance and told him to teach it to all the people. He said that if all the Indians danced this dance, the buffalo would return, their dead killed in the wars with the whites would return, and the grass would come back. We had a prophet like that too at Ash Creek."

"Jesus again. What happened?" I asked.

"Jesus was a Jew. Jews were Israelites. Israelites were tribal peoples. The Mormons, they even trace the Israelite connection to the American Indian." Phillip shrugged.

"No, I mean what happened to Wovoka and the other prophet?"

"The same thing happened that always happens to all prophets. They were murdered by the Army. Even though they advocated peaceful dancing only, when Indians start dancing and singing, the intensity of the spirituality of it scares whites. So they killed them. Not that it's always the enemy that kills its prophets. As often as not, it's their own people. Look at Crazy Horse, murdered by his own people and soldiers both, or *Yeshua*, the Romans killed him but his own people called for his death."

He was silent for a moment, looking into the distance. "People hate their prophets and their dreamers. The better they are, the more it scares 'em. All Jesus said was to love each other, not heterosexually, not just platonically, not just your friends and family, but enemies too. That scared the crap out 'em. So they crucified him. Ever hear of General Billy Mitchell?"

I shook my head.

"He is the father of the Air Force. He was a bi-plane pilot in World War One. Hero made general. Predicted the attack on Pearl Harbor in detail twenty years before it happened. Before the damn planes were even capable of flying that far. While the Japs were still our allies."

"Really," I was amazed.

"Guess what they did to him?" Phillip stared at me.

"Medal of Honor?" I asked.

"They demoted him, court-martialed him, ridiculed and mocked him and forced him to retire."

"Why?" I was truly at a loss.

"Folks like their prophets dead and buried and safely out of the way. When we are around, seeing things they don't, it scares them too much." He stared out into the distance, lost in his own sad ruminations. And it will happen to me too, in the end." He broke his trance-like stare and looked at me. "You, too, if you go far enough."

I eerily recall that day—the day Phillip prophesized his own death. He would die after being brutally assaulted on San Carlos, his own reservation, and by his own people, jealous of his success and fame. The same fate seems to befall all great prophets and spiritual leaders, not just those in ancient times like Jesus. Fools Crow, the legendary Lakota shaman and contemporary of Phillip, was similarly attacked and subsequently died.

Years later, I would meet the Tom Mails, the famous Lutheran minister, Indian biographer, author and student of Fools Crow and Phillip. He would tell me of Fools Crow's fate—also at the hands of his own people, driven by greed and jealousy of his fame and support by such stars as Robert Diniro, who used to buy his groceries. Murdered for groceries and good works seems to be a common theme among prophets and profiteers.

Many come to quickly resent the gifts of freedom and enlightenment, for with enlightenment comes an awful awareness of spiritual adulthood, and with the freedom, an accompanying responsibility. True spiritual prophecy brings change and change oft times upsets the apple cart. And woe to those who come between the apples and the lotus-apple eaters.

Over the years, I realize now that this freedom terrifies the many who would rather hold onto their wounds, keep an endless score of the wrongs done them, and cling to the past and their egotistical views of the world like some kind of clam, clamped to a rock and closed to the magnificence of the sea around it.

But that day I chose to let go—of fear, anger and self-pity. I forgot the scorecard, and chose to move forward. My heart soared with the freedom I alone had given myself. I was swept with a wave of gratitude to Phillip.

I was lighter and free in a way I had never been before. I vowed then and there never to be controlled by others in any way, and certainly not by emotional manipulation. I was so elated I had missed some of Phillip's words.

"—are conquered. The buffalo wiped out. So with all this empty space the ranchers start raising the most stupid, most helpless creature on God's green earth—the cow. Now cows are a fatty meat and high in cholesterol. They are also helpless." He tapped the dash.

"Cows. They fall prey to the wolves 'cause they can't defend themselves. So what do the new white ranchers do? They kill off all the wolves. But then the cows break their legs in gopher holes, so what next? The ranchers kill off the gophers."

"But," Phillip poked a hole in the air, "eventually people start figuring all this out, and they start raising buffalo. The buffalo can defend itself against wolves and it doesn't break legs in gopher holes, and the meat is lean and even low in cholesterol—so the buffalo are returning. And white people now are concerned about the environment—so the grass is coming back. People like you want to learn about their native heritage, so their relations are returning. Not the dead ones but the new, living, lost ones—like you."

"Of course," he chuckled, "none of this is happening on a human schedule or as Wovoka visualized. But it is happening—on *Ulsen's* schedule."

"So you're saying that the natural luminous way of America is the buffalo and the grass?"

"And the Indian way. We were physically conquered, but now we are spiritually conquering. You know what Benjamin Franklin wanted as the animal totem for the new United States? The turkey. But what won out?"

"The eagle, of course." I was happy to be able to have some answers. Phillip nodded.

"But," he raised an index finger, "what was the animal most sacred to all Indian nations on Turtle Island—what we now call America?"

I smiled as I got it. "The eagle. So everyone reaches the same conclusions because these aren't based on opinions but spiritual, universal truths."

"Okay, that's it for today."

"Wait a minute, we haven't even discussed what happened today," I protested.

"Not right now."

"Why not?"

"Because we're back. And I'm pretty sure Harlyn wants his truck back now."

We pulled into Phillip's place. Gokliya stepped out the door.

"Well, when are we going to talk about him?"

"We already did. That conversation is closed and you will show respect to all of your elders." It was not a request but a command. Gokliya was walking over.

"But what about what happened—don't we need to debrief?"

"We'll do that next month, when you're healed up and ready to go." Gokliya was at the driver door, glaring at me.

"Go where?"

"Up Mount Wrightson. You're running up that next." He smiled, watching my mouth drop open.

"Huh?" I stuttered.

"Besides your *keiban* are now properly broke in and wet-fitted to your feet."

He pointed with his chin towards my feet. I looked down. It was true. After the scoring, the long run, and the soaking, the mocks were now dry and perfectly contoured to my feet.

Gokliya jerked open the car door. I turned off the ignition and got out, tossing him the keys. He caught them and brushed past me, shooting me a glance that dripped daggers. He got in and slammed the door, then cranked the engine. But Phillip still sat in the passenger seat.

As I moved slowly to my car, I strained to hear their conversation. As I came around the front of the pick-up, I moved back towards the pick-up's open passenger window. As I did, their voices picked up and wafted to me.

"...why teach these *Ligaiye'e*? Why?... have stolen everything from us...now they want our religion?"

I was pausing at my car door, fumbling with the keys while straining to eavesdrop. Suddenly Phillip's clear, calm voice drifted to me.

"...not ours to keep, only ours to give...the Ghost Dance comes true...but not our way and not our choice...to whomever is worthy, and he alone...has shown up."

Then there was only silence. I glanced over. They were both looking at me and I couldn't decide whose stare was harder. I got in my car and drove off quickly. I remember when I walked into my dorm, the guy at the front desk thought I had been in a car wreck.

The next day I could barely get out of bed. I did only to pee. Then I went back to sleep. I took the following day off from classes as well. By Wednesday I was hobbling around campus like an old man, students eyeing my scabbing knees and elbows with revulsion and curiosity.

Several skate-heads told me sincerely to "pad up bro." I didn't have the stones to tell them that I had just lost a hand-to-hand fight with Geronimo.

Three weeks later I reluctantly showed up at Phillip's. He was standing in the doorway sipping coffee. It was five in the morning and still dark, but there he was leaning in the doorway.

"*Dagote'e, shiye,*" he called as he got into my car.

"*Shilgonte'e,*" I answered without a lot of conviction, "where to?"

"Already told you. South on nineteen to Madera Canyon."

"So I'm running up Mount Wrightson?"

"Yup."

"What about Gokliya?"

"Harlyn's not here. The mountain is. Be here now. Stop keeping score. There's no point. 'Cause it ain't ever going to be even. Anybody ever call you a prairie nigger?"

"No sir, why?"

"Well, since you are so eager to talk about Harlyn, I thought you might have something in common—guess not." He set his empty coffee cup on the dash.

"Now let's get back to power gait."

"What?"

"Power gait, didn't…never mind. Pay attention. All indigenous people are famous runners. We had to be able to run down game, run into or from battle, run messages or medicine or, just like the Tarahumara down in the Madres in Mexico, run to get around. But sometimes physical running is not enough. Like the Spartan at Marathon." He looked at me expectantly.

I scratched my head and shrugged.

"Nike!" He looked again.

He groaned and looked up comically. "How can I teach him about unconventional truth if he doesn't even know conventional history? The Spartans won a great victory at Marathon. A single runner was sent to convey the news. He made the long, grueling twenty-six mile run back to Sparta totally spent and delivered the news in one word—'Nike'—which means victory, then keeled over dead. That's where all those terms come from, son."

"Oh, that Marathon and Nike," I dead-panned.

"Yeah, that one," Phillip intoned dryly. "Anyway, the Spartan died just then—do you think that was coincidence or that he was already physically spent and had to rely on some other part of himself to complete his duty as a man and Spartan warrior?"

"He had to rely on his spiritual side."

"And if his physical body was spent, but he still had the duty to his circle, then what side of himself would he rely on?"

"Spiritual, grandfather."

"So to do this, we turn physical running into prayer, a form of moving meditation that goes beyond physical technique, that unifies the spiritual and physical and then, as the physical body weakens, it reveals and strengthens—" He looked over at me and put out his left hand palm up.

"The spiritual." Again it was so simple and elegant a truth I didn't understand how I could not have seen it before, and I said so. "Oh, that makes perfect sense. Once you teach me these things, they are obvious, as if I had even known them but forgotten them."

"These are truths that babies know, but then as they learn modern, first-world industrial ways and language for this world, they forget, and it's replaced with the intellectualism of materialism. Baby babble isn't—it's angelic, we just have forgotten that language."

I pondered this. So many times Phillip would say things that were totally unexpected and did not seem to come from an Apache or even Indian perspective.

It was only many years later before I finally realized that he had achieved a level of spiritual enlightenment that had transcended his own culture and society. That is why he was so effective in both the native and non-native worlds. It was why he was able to do so much—not only for his own people. But his spiritual under-standing allowed him to go even further, transcend his world, and teach me, which then allowed me to reach out and help the larger non-Indian society that had conquered his own.

"So I see your *keiban* are now formed to your feet."

"Yes, sir—the hard way."

"And you know to run on your hooves or pads—the balls of your feet. Keep your arms low or no more than parallel to the ground. Don't ball up your fist. It will tense up your entire body and make it hard to go far. Just lean slightly forward, so your spine is off line with the vertical impact of your stride. Keep your feet under-neath you. Breathe in through your nose, pause and out through your mouth. Watch your breath and then your heart slow."

"Yes sir. You know when I was running, I got so exhausted I felt I was being pulled along by—"

"A line from your belly?" Phillip interrupted.

"Exactly, how did you know?"

"That is the gait of power. You have already begun to experi-ence it. But conversely your physical body still needs to be strong enough to withstand the rigors when *diyi* kicks in. This is different from the endorphins that kick in, but they help too. Because after you run to battle or to flee, you will as a man and a warrior have other immediate duties—like fighting enemies or rescuing the in-nocent. Because that is what a warrior does: place himself between evil and innocence through selfless service. That is why Harlyn was fighting with a paper blade with you afterwards."

"Wait a minute, you mean he was supposed to do that? He was supposed to fight with me? I thought he was just angry at me?"

"He was fierce. Real men are fierce. Boys get angry. Fierceness is different than anger. Fierceness focuses our attention to gather our intention, thus allowing us to still win in battle even when we are outnumbered and exhausted—whether this battle is physical as in the old days when Harlyn's great granddad held off two U.S. Armies with only six warriors; or now when Vine is battling the federal courts for our treaty rights." His voice was smooth as always but his eyes were hard and sharp with intensity. I realized he was showing me by projecting at that very moment the ferocity required of Apache manhood.

"But a true man and warrior must possess this fierceness of focus, to do those intense hard things that women should not have to, and do not do as well as us anyway."

"Like what?"

"Like war and fighting. Or do you believe all those TV shows and movies that show *Charlie's Angels* beating up big guys?"

"No. I'm a black belt. I've seen enough fights to know that. So I was wrong about Harlyn."

"I thought we had already established that. Pull off here." I pulled off just at the base of the road up Wrightson . Unlike Lemon, the road ended just ahead and became instead a dirt hiking trail that faded into the pre-dawn darkness. To the right I could hear the sound of water rushing over rocks in a nearby stream.

"*Ugash.*" Phillip hopped out and trotted off into the dark.

"Uh—okay." I hopped and locked up, then trotted off after Phillip. Somehow he was already about fifty feet ahead up the steep trail. I sprinted to catch up.

I tripped, then stumbled and slowed my pace down. I looked down for a moment at my moccasins. When I looked up, Phillip was even further up the trail. I realized that I could not lengthen my stride to catch up and stay in power gait form. Instead I decided this was yet another lesson. As I watched Phillip closely ahead, he was certainly not hurrying. In fact he appeared to be barely running, moving almost at a fast walk. But I realized, the efficiency of his movement was impeccable. There was simply nothing wasted in his movement. I decided to concentrate on moving out impeccably and keeping Phillip in sight since the trail was difficult to discern in the darkness. But I kept tripping so I called out, "I can't stay on the trail."

"See," he called back.

"See what? That's the problem," I called out in exasperation.

"My track."

"But I can't—it's dark."

"Not my physical track." His voice wafted back to me.

"Oh." I relaxed my gaze and after a couple of steps my luminous vision clicked in. There was a slight glow around every rock and all over the ground, a lot like moonlight.

And then I saw it. On the trail up ahead I saw a couple of bright patches fading rapidly as I approached. I saw a little further up and saw more of them. It was several steps before I finally realized I was seeing, and seeing Phillip's tracks, but luminously.

"That's amazing," I yelled.

"You ain't seen nothing yet, kid," he called over his shoulder.

Now that I could see the trail luminously, I stopped tripping and was able to establish a better pace. Because of the uneven terrain I lowered my hips even more and bent my knees a bit more.

As soon as the balls of my rawhide feet hit the ground the stretched scoring bit into the dirt and gripped it momentarily. Then I let my foot slide up and kick at my own butt lightly.

My stride became light, quick and efficient, and my pace picked up even as I felt my breath slowing. I smiled in the darkness and inhaled deeply and slowly through my nose.

It was fun watching Phillip's tracks in the distance. It was my own private light show. I closed the distance a bit and could see them right after his foot strike. They were brightest as his foot lifted up, and then they began to quickly fade. By the time I covered the thirty yards or so between us, they were nearly gone. I realized I was luminously tracking Phillip. That was pretty cool.

The groove of the run sustained me for the first hour or so, then I began to tire. Then the dawn began to break. I ran through the gray mist. Sometime during the next hour my endorphins kicked in. The scab on my right knee cracked open, but the endorphins numbed the pain.

By the third hour I was tiring greatly. The trail had narrowed from disuse and steepened considerably. I looked up for Phillip and something knocked me lightly on the head. Something plopped at my feet. I stopped and picked it up. It was a small, pine cone. It was my first. Later I would learn that it would not be my last, and that as a mountain people the Apache had many uses for pine cones.

"Gotta do better than that," Phillip said, leaning lightly against a pine off to the side of the trail. I jumped like I had been electrocuted.

He looked rested, as if he had been there all night not running up this mountain with me. I was thirty years his junior and in great shape, but the pace and altitude were already getting to me. He resumed his relentless trot.

"What?"

"Knowing. Now that you can see, you should feel as well. Then you'll just know," he called over his shoulder. "You need to be able to feel things before they hit your family, if you are going to lead them."

He was gone again. I was breathless, sore, and thirsty. I took a long swig of water from the canteen in my little daypack, stowed it and trotted off. But now every step was leaden. The stop had made me static and given me a chance to feel the lactic acid build up in my muscles and the soreness in my bones. The beginning of a dehydration headache clawed at my skull. The next mile pounded my feet, ankles, knees, hips, spine and neck. Even though I was still on the balls of my feet, I was too tired to maintain that strike and I came down on my heel after jarring my entire skeletal structure. Each foot-strike felt like a little punch.

I ran on and on endlessly. Again my world became a stride, then the next the next. But I wasn't near passing out this time. Just bone tired and sore.

Abruptly I rounded yet another corner. A gorgeous panoramic vista opened up and out before me with each step. It wasn't the peak but it was a spectacular spot and we had to be near it. Phillip stood before me erect, hands on his hips. Behind him was the dawn sky. Off to the mountainside an improbable waterfall crashed down noisily and cut the trail rock in half with years of the flow neatly rounding off the sharp edges. A spray that painted a permanent waterfall in the rays of the rising sun, misted around us.

"Wow, waterfall, rainbow and rising sun!" I said.

"Under," he said and pointed to the waterfall.

"How? I'll fall."

"Straddle the rocks and raise your arms—and see."

Exhausted as I was, it would have been easy to slip and fall over the trail edge. Phillip himself stood nonchalantly near the edge. I took a deep breath and stepped out into space. My right moccasin found the slippery right rock face, my left found the left. I faced outwards into the brightening gold of the dawn sun. My legs trembled uncontrollably with fatigue and cold.

The water hit my back like a great, icy thump, and then continued to pound me. I grunted as the air shot out of me, then gasped as the near freezing water slanted off me in all directions. My body quaked with the cold and something more—like an electric current pulsing through. Then I realized as Phillip had said, there was just such a current running through me and somehow I had just jump-started it.

"See!" I heard Phillip call to me.

I opened my eyes and extended my arms out and up. The world flashed into a high definition, crystal sharp, neon bright, realm of luminous halos and shades. Everything glowed and pulsed in one great crash of light.

I had never seen so clearly or cleanly before. I could even see little halos around the individual water droplets spewed from the falls. The rainbow was doubled as I saw un-named colors past the visible spectrum of infrared and ultraviolet. Tiny micro rainbows revealed themselves around the mini halos of the water drops. I was enthralled and entranced. It was quite literally, glorious.

"Here." Phillip's voice drew my attention to him.

The sunrise struck him and turned him red bronze with a gold neon halo fading to a near complete spectrum around him. Around him was a thick, purple-blue fog that swirled and meandered about his fiery form. The halo of luminosity around him flashed occasionally like mini-lightning strikes, and tiny sparks of luminous fire orbited and drifted around and up from him. He was brighter than the dawn.

"Step out of there now," he said.

I carefully shifted my weight to the left and with a great effort lifted my right leg off the rock and across the chasm and over to the left side of the trailhead. I set it down and it folded under me. I went down hard.

I realized my leg had somehow gone numb straddling the falls. For an instant I feared I had broken it. But then I ran my hands quickly over the cold hunk of meat and massaged it until feeling began to painfully return.

"See," Phillip commanded.

Almost immediately I saw his dreaming body move sharply out to the right of him. It too pulsed and glowed. It was amazing to watch. The dreaming body returned to Phillip proper and then proceeded to emerge from the left side of him. It separated out an upright body length away, paused, then slowly faded back into Phillip.

I opened my mouth to speak and Phillip raised his hand. Now his luminous body emerged above him, straight up, until it was as if Phillip was standing upon his own shoulders. Then after a beat, the light body faded back down, till I again focused on Phillip's smile alone.

"Up," I heard Phillip order in a stern voice I was unused to. I looked up and shifted back to normal sight. In each hand unbelievably, was a stick. He tossed one at my feet. I shook my head.

"Now? This is a bad dream," I muttered.

"No, this is manhood training. As a man you will never be attacked when you are rested, ready and prepared. It will always be when you are off balance, exhausted and unready. Like now." He grinned. "Up."

I sighed and climbed to my feet. Phillip thumped me on the head with the stick and I moved to block it only after.

"Ow!"

"Men don't show pain or panic. It scares the women and kids." He struck again on my right throat. This time I struck his stick arm simultaneously.

"Left side," Phillip warned as he struck just as he said he would, at my left throat. Again I tied his strike with mine.

"I'm too tired."

"I know," he said. "Now, you attack."

I sighed deeply and then lunged with what little energy I could bring to bear. Phillip countered my arm before it was ever even near him.

"Again," Phillip commanded.

I jabbed straight in and faster this time, as my young body recovered. But once again Phillip sidestepped me in seeming slow motion, then struck my own arm and throat.

I shook my head. "Okay, you got me just like Gokliya."

"Grow up, boy!" Phillip's voice slapped me with such sudden stridency that I jolted. "This time when I attack—see."

I shifted to luminous vision in a moment. Phillip seemed to know because that is when his luminous form started to swing at my left. I parried automatically. Then his physical arm followed and I caught his arm with my branch before he could touch me!

"Wait, what just—" I stuttered. But Phillip interrupted.

"Quiet. Keep seeing."

This time I saw his dreaming body swing towards my right. I instinctively parried and sure enough again, I met Phillip's physical arm—stopping it this time *before* it touched my arm.

Suddenly the dreaming arm flared directly at me. I sidestepped and parried, but met only air. After a moment Phillip's stick tapped my hand lightly. I looked up. He was smiling, and so I realized, was I.

"Gotta wait till the physical strike actually comes," he drawled, "if, of course, it's a physical fight."

"That's incredible," I gushed.

"That," Phillip replied, "is only the beginning."

"Wait, what do you mean a physical fight?"

"All physical, human battles originate in spiritual warfare, between Bob—as you call it, and evil. We are, after all, all children born of war."

"What do you mean?"

He shook his head. "Manhood first. Warriorship later. Are you recovered?"

"Yes, sir, I guess."

"Can you strike me now? Fast, with all the speed of your youth?"

"Yes, sir, I think so."

"Then do it now, as fast as you can."

I thought about driving straight in at Phillip's throat. Almost simultaneously I launched at him. But Phillip was already moving, even slower than before, but he was out of the way of my strike long before I even got there. Phillip was now standing next to me smiling, an arm on my shoulder, his own stick lightly tapping at my throat.

"So that's what you meant—fight without weapons and go beyond the physical," I mused. "That's how they did it."

"That's how we still do it."

"What now?" I asked.

"Now, we get a good drink of this sweet water." Phillip walked over to the falls and stuck his hand out, cupped it and slurped up the cold water. I followed suit.

We started down the mountain in silence. Phillip put his hand on my shoulder to steady himself, but I think it steadied me more. A couple of miles downhill we veered off across the stream, up a hill and into a small clearing.

"You are goin' to love this one," Phillip laughed, "Lay down on your back, arms at your sides, legs uncrossed and close your eyes."

"Yes!" I dropped onto my back and emitted a long, fake snore.

"Very funny. Now establish a good, slow breathing cycle, then slow your heart, then quiet your mind." He grew silent to give me a couple of minutes to accomplish the tasks. I was so exhausted, it did not take me long this time. Almost at once, I drifted off to sleep. The next thing I remember was Phillip gently kicking the sole of my moccasin.

"No sleepin' on the job. Interlink your thumb and index fingers on each hand just over your solar plexus. That'll keep you awake. I want you just on the line between sleep and wakefulness, between dreaming and physical."

I linked my fingers—like a two-handed okay sign. It worked. Even though I was bone-tired and ready to sleep, it was as if I had completed a circuit. I stayed just on the edge of sleep, totally relaxed but awake. It was strange, because as I watched my breathing, I would drift in and out of dreams even though I would return to wakefulness. It was a place I had never been before, as if I was standing in a doorway, leaning at first into one room and then back into the other—and all of it happening within the pulse of something, not my heart nor my breathing, but something even more primordial.

"Good, now without moving your physical form, with no movement of your flesh-and-blood body, raise your right hand by bending at the elbow."

I thought about this one for a moment. Then I imagined myself lifting my arm. Phillip must have been a mind reader as well because he immediately said, "Don't imagine lifting your hand. When you want to fly in your physical form—it's not designed properly for flight unless you're a witch, so you imagine an airplane and then build it—but to fly in dreaming body you just watch it happen. Just watch your dreaming hand rise up."

I tried again, just trying to watch it happen.

"Nope, keep trying."

I tried again, pretending to move my hand.

"Nope, stop pretending imagining and trying not to try. Just like seeing, this is a special kind of non-effort, let go, and just watch it happen."

I suspended my disbelief and relaxed, then I just watched myself or rather my luminous self.

"*Enju,*" Phillip's voice called to me. "That's it and that's enough for today. Get up."

"Huh, what's it?" I was barely awake and had no idea what time it was or where I was.

"Get on up, that was just fine." Phillip squatted down next to me. "You can get up, can't you?"

"Of course I can get up," I said, struggling to open my eyes and, succeeding in that task, trying to raise my head and arms. After a moment my head came up, swiveled about like a turtle emerging from its shell, and then fell back.

"Yup, was afraid of that," he chuckled.

"Afraid...of what?" I drawled out slowly.

"Tired, huh?"

"Maybe, just a bit. Why what happened to me?" I succeeded in shaking my feet and flexing my fingers. Next I started to work slightly flexing my legs.

"Well, you can run up mountains just fine, but you've never really used your dreaming body before. So you tire easily like a newborn when you do. You'll get used to it."

"What part of dreaming body did I use and when?"

"Back there when I told you to raise your luminous hand up. You did it finally."

"I don't remember that," I said, getting my legs bent enough to bring my feet underneath me.

"That's because you didn't know you could see anything when you did. Just like a little, blind baby. When a baby first sees, they don't know what to make of what they are seeing and they don't know how to focus on each object. First, they don't even know they are seeing."

He grabbed my shoulders and hauled me up to sitting position. "They then see dark and light—appropriately enough. Then they start to discern shapes and details. So first they see a light egg shape. Then an egg shape with spots on it. Then eventually a face appears with eyes."

He stood up with a tight grip on my shoulders again and I came up with him. "Quickly after that the baby learns what the movements and changes, the expressions on the face mean. And at the same time that baby is kicking and squirming and rolling around. And all that is exercising its body."

He let go and I stood there wobbling like a two-year-old. "That's what you are now—a grown physical man but a spiritual baby. You're learning to see and now you just started to exercise your dreamin' body—when you raised your hand. So you are tired from that."

"You mean," I replied slowly, "I'm not tired from the run. You're saying I'm tired from just lifting my hand—my dreaming hand up once?"

"Well, you tried to lift it up several times and your arms and even your torso. But you just twitched around luminously for a while too. Don't worry, you are going to start exercising luminously now too." He slapped me on the back and the momentum propelled me forward—and almost face down. We headed down hill.

"When you sleep, your dreaming body is the other side of yourself. It has to come and move around. Just like your physical body needs to move around to maintain its muscle fitness and bone structure."

"So that's why we have to dream and have REM sleep," I mused.

"That's why. It's the other half of us—of our soul. Now, each night when you go to sleep, you link your fingers on your chest...."

"Over my soul?"

"Over the place where your soul sits normally."

"And just before you go to sleep, you focus on lifting your dreamin' head up, then lift your dream hands up and look at 'em with your dreamin' eyes."

"That's a lot of dreaming body work."

"You're just getting started. Now, you can buy me dinner in Green Valley."

"You are goin' to love this one!"

Lay down on your back, arms at your sides, legs uncrossed and close your eyes.

Now establish a good, slow breathing cycle.

Then slow your heart.

Now quiet your mind.

Interlink your thumb and index fingers on each hand just over your solar plexus. That'll keep you awake.

Drift to the line between sleep and wakefulness, between dreaming and physical.

Now without moving your physical form, with no movement of your flesh and blood body, raise your right hand by bending at the elbow.

Just watch it happen.

Just watch your dreaming hand rise up.

Keep trying.

Just like seeing, this is a special kind of non-effort; let go and just watch it happen.

Don't worry about proving you were successful or not. You would need a partner that could see to know for sure. The point is to have the skill for when you need it.

To do the impossible.

In selfless service.

For someone else.

NOVICE TIME

You always work as a group, not somebody singled out.
There is no such thing as that with the Apache.
—Phillip Cassadore

F OR THE NEXT FOUR WEEKS I went to class but in reality my college training revolved around my training with Phillip. Class was a dreary, predictable monotony of intellectualism that no longer touched me. But every meeting with Phillip was a visceral encounter that left me with an electric charge. After each meet I was incandescent and forever changed.

I ran every day and everywhere. When I wasn't running, I did push-ups and sit-ups. I became physically strong in my legs, belly and arms, and I thought in my dreaming body as well. The physical train-up was the easy part. I simply did a few more of whatever exercise I was doing each time. I did my physical exercises a little longer, harder and faster each time.

The tricky part was the spiritual. Phillip had told me to be humble but now fierce, and masculine in the extreme. But to him that meant watching over everyone near me, making sure all kids and women around me were safe, and seeing if every adult man was an enemy or friend. Now I was to look everyone in the eye and step aside for no one. If some one wanted a fight, I was to be willing to oblige. I knocked into several passing jocks on my way to class on different occasions, but I found no one really wanted to swing. Several wanted to talk tough, but then moved off when I stood my ground.

I was passing by Bear Down Gym on the U of A campus one morning when I banged shoulders with a Wildcat lineman.

"Watch it, punk," the deep voice boomed out. I looked back unmoved and in silence.

"I said, watch it."

"I heard you the first time." Normally I would have had the sense to move off, but Phillip had been specific about his instruction. In my empowerment cycle I was to back down from no one nor step aside for anybody.

"Well, you better clean out your freaking ears or I'll clean 'em out for you."

"You gonna talk me to death," I said slowly staring into his eyes, "or fight?"

He stared back at me blankly. I don't think anybody had stood up to him since high school. He was a massive hulk of bone and muscle, but Geronimo I recalled had been skinny and rather short. Size and bulk was not the determining factor in a fight. Willingness was. And at that moment I was totally willing and ready to go.

"Well," I said, pushing the situation. "I'm getting real bored just standing here."

Without noticing, luma-vision, as I had begun to call it to myself, kicked in and I saw the linebacker's massive dreaming body launch itself at me. I sidestepped just ahead of his physical body and he went charging past me. He stopped and turned, clearly furious for missing his first tackle in a long time. He lunged again and I moved easily aside again this time barely even seeing his physical form. A couple of coeds walked by and giggled. When he turned back, I could tell he was now completely consumed by rage.

He lunged again in complete fury and with all of two hundred and fifty pounds.

But this time I left my foot out as I pivoted and he went down face first deep into the dirt. He pushed himself up with both hands just as I swung my backpack off my right shoulder with my left hand and smacked him hard with it, and the two hard-bound textbooks inside to the back of his head. He grunted and ate dirt. I let the backpack drop alongside his head and reached under grabbing a strap. I brought it up violently and crossed my arms choking him hard with the strap.

His face went red, then purple. Right before his physical hands came up, I saw him lead with his dreaming ones, so I released the strap, swinging the pack free. He sprung up and back like he was coming off a trampoline. I pivoted again but continued in a full turn and let my momentum swing the pack in a wide arc right into his face. His nose exploded with a crunch and a spray of blood. He went down on his ass hard.

I stood over him and actually thought about taking his scalp, though Apaches did not do that. He looked up at me holding his nose. Blood dripped between his fingers.

"Ah, I'll get benched for squashing you, screw yourself." I stood there still. Finally he climbed up on his feet and he walked off, but around me and quickly.

Dreaming was harder. The first week I just went to sleep, forgetting to interlock my fingers. When I remembered to do that, I didn't sleep at all the first two nights. The third night I focused my attention on my breathing and heartbeat, slowing both, but then I just drifted off. But the next couple of nights I got used to bringing myself to the edge of sleep and I began to find that I could shift attention from my physical point of view to the spiritual or dreaming viewpoint.

A couple of nights later I raised my head in dreaming body. I remember it clearly because everything took on a whitish glow. It was an unmistakable view from the luminous side.

Several days later I was consistently raising my head each night and even looking briefly around the room. Then I began to work on raising my hands. The next night I was fairly certain I had managed to raise my hands, so I raised my head. Sure enough, in white-light luminous vision I saw luminous hands glowing incandescently and rise up from my prone hands.

But the perspective was strange. It did not automatically correspond to my physical form. Usually my assemblage point of view in dreaming was at least a head higher than in physical form. Perspective changes were downright disturbing. It wasn't like turning your head in the physical world and seeing the landscape in between and then whatever you were looking at. One moment you would be staring at a bookshelf and then suddenly you were looking down from it. It was a strange, almost indescribable kind of vertigo that I have never experienced before or since.

The next morning I was not sleepy but tired, and it took me longer than usual to get out of bed. The following Saturday night, while my peers were drinking and partying at Homecoming, I was excited because I had raised my luminous arms straight up and out.

Sunday morning I showed up at Phillip's. He hopped in my car and we drove a short trip out west to the Saguaro Mountains. On the way I told Phillip what I had achieved. He didn't seem surprised. He just nodded and said, *"Enju."*

"By the way, what's the blanket for?" Phillip had a light, buff-colored blanket folded, wrapped and draped over one shoulder and tied at the opposite hip. Draped across the opposite shoulder was a small gourd, curved like a woman, with a cork in it.

"And what's with the gourd? It's not Halloween," I wise-cracked.

"You'll see," was all he'd say.

In less than a half an hour he told me to pull off onto a dirt road off Ajo. We bumped along the dirt track for another fifteen minutes until we reached the base of a small rock mountain with a jagged rock top.

"That's it. That's all I got to run up today," I said. These were small, rocky mounts that didn't even go high up into altitude enough to have pines growing on them—only Saguaro. I was grinning.

"Glad you feel that way," he grinned right back. "Ready?"

"Ready," I shot back.

"Good, but first take a gulp—but don't swallow it." He unslung then unplugged the gourd and handed it to me. Then he pulled a tiny plastic cup from his shirt pocket and black magic marker. He marked the waterline on the top outside of the cup with the Sharpie marker. "See that?"

"Yes, sir."

"When you reach the top, that's how much water I expect you to spit back in this cup—all this water, right to the line."

"Come again?"

"This is an old Apache test. To bring water to a wounded warrior or carry it to a child when you had no canteen or *tuus*. Questions?"

"What happens if I swallow it?"

"No problem, you can run it again," he grinned. "A better question is what happens if you don't."

"Okay, what happens if I don't?"

"Find out." He handed me the cup. I swallowed, and then slowly sipped the water, making sure I could hold it all in my mouth. When I found I could hold it all, I nodded and took off.

I quickly found out that while I was now in excellent running shape, breathing only through my nose was a whole new experience. I had to make my stride even smoother, and slow my heart even more. Breathing through my nose alone, my brain felt more oxygenated and everything seemed sharper and in finer focus.

And when I shifted to luminous vision, the difference in focus was even more dramatic. I could see more the pulse of each of the individual halos around each rock and every branch even more clearly. Many years later I would learn about yogic nasal breathing traditions, and that science too had proved that nitric oxide is breathed in through the nose.

Nitric oxide dilates the pulmonary vessels fifteen to twenty percent more than does mouth breathing. This means that we are breathing deeper and better when we breathe in and out through the nose.

I stopped abruptly and looked to the right. Phillip was standing off to the side behind a huge Saguaro, a rock in his hand—ready to toss. He smiled and let the rock drop, then pointed up the trail. I was trying to figure out how he had gotten ahead of me when he took off. I followed close behind. Then it hit me. Or rather it didn't. I had just avoided Phillip's famous pine cone ambush—except this time it would have been a rock!

I ran on, but now lightly, happily, the balls of my feet just barely dusting the trail. The endorphins kicked in, and then shortly after that something else did as well. I began to glide above the ground and I was simply pulled along from my center. My stride was effortless and easy, and I could have run on forever and for the rest of my life.

But Phillip was standing in front of me at the top. Behind him the sun was rising. He held out the cup. I took it and gently and carefully spit the water back into the cup. It came up to level. We both looked at each other.

"Now pour it out, but toward you out of reverence for *tu*—for the water of life that fills us and forms us and sustains us. Make the pouring itself a prayer of recognition and respect and thanks."

I was dying of thirst but I took the cup and knelt down and poured the water out slowly towards me. "And now that water is in the earth. But it's still water." I grinned.

Phillip nodded and smiled. "Stand up and watch." He faced the rising sun, hands over his groin.

"Put your hands just off and over your groin, thumb almost touching, index fingers pointing down and almost touching as well. Feel the heat and current between your fingers and your palms and groin. Can you feel it?"

It took a moment but I could feel a pulse of energy and heat between my thumbs, fingers and radiating between my palms and off my groin. I was pulsing all over from the run. He inhaled deeply and slowly raised his arms straight to the rising sun which was just cresting the distant mountain range.

"Do as I do." Phillip coached. "Slowly inhale as you watch your hands and arms raise themselves to greet the dawn. That is, let your dreaming body lead the raising of your physical arms."

That was a new one. I slowly began to raise my arms, but then something wild happened. I stopped trying to raise my arms and watched as they continued to float up slowly on their own.

The dawn's rays spilled over the distant mountain top in individual rays, slanting directly into my eyes. I squinted in the brilliance as the dawn sky brightened into day.

"Let *sha* rays spill into your squinted pupils, moving your eyes and head from right to left, empowering and warming you deep inside. But as the sun clears the ridge, don't look directly a it; it will just blind you." As he spoke he was doing it, slowly so I could follow.

"Instead, place your thumb and index finger just touching. You'll form your own Morningstar eclipse. Morningstar is another name for we use for *Yeshua*. You'll see why."

My arms came up at face level and then I slowly brought them together—elbows bent, thumbs and index fingers all touching. The space in between formed a star-shaped void. Years later I would see the exact same shape in Japan in the form of a ninja moon *shuriken* and *kuji* finger weaving position called *pyo*, or appropriately enough "power." I would also see it painted on Apache mountain spirit dancers, and eventually would paint it countless times on my own dance teams.

I brought the star-shaped opening of my fingers in front of the now risen sun. The main blinding white fireball was blocked. Instead a shining, white light cross magically appeared, exactly like the flag of New Mexico. It was incredible. It spread out around me and past me in the four directions, expanding as it went. The cardinal points were filled with the sun rays as they shot outward, shining and blinding. At the cross's tips the edges were V-shaped, like a Templar cross, and I wondered if there was a connection since they had been the most mystical of all knights. I felt the warmth of the sun on my palms and fingertips. In a flash of enlightenment I realized that this is what the biblical Saul must have seen and changed him to the Christian Paul—and what Constantine too had seen in the sky and afterwards converted his kingdom to Christianity. And it was still there. It was even on the New Mexico state flag. For anyone who had eyes to see—or the training of an Apache holy man.

But then something else happened. I filtered the rays of the shining cross into the pupils of my eyes and, as I did, a current of energy surged through me and up me from my groin along my spine up through my belly, chest, throat, and up to the crown of my head. All these areas, these energy centers on me, were suddenly very hot, like burners that had just been lit. I began sweating profusely.

"*Enju*. Now let your fingers and hands spread apart and see."

I let my fingers part and saw the clear, bright outline of my luminosity around my hands. But there was something more, something new. As my hands moved further apart, the luminosity trailed off of my fingertips like wisps of incandescent smoke. I left ten glowing trails of light in the air tracing the air around me. It was as if I had painted a luminous egg shape around my form.

"Now come slowly down along your sides, exhaling as you go, until your fingers reunite again …just …over, and your groin." He finished just as he completed the complete arc.

I followed suit. But now my fingers and palms burned with inner heat. So did my groin, solar plexus, chest, throat and forehead, as well as the crown of my head. It was as if a sun lamp had been placed on these spots.

"Put your hand up against the sky and see," Phillip commanded.

I did and saw not only the normal luminosity around my hand but a glow on it. Then in a moment I saw a blue-violet light pulsing. After a couple of moments I realized that it was matching the beat of my own heart. It was if the battery of my being had for the first time been fully charged. I felt young and strong and bursting with *diyi*.

"Sit now in warrior seat. Keep your back straight. Chin tucked. Tongue—"

"On the roof of my mouth." I finished his sentence.

Phillip took the blanket from his shoulder and draped it over my head and around my torso, like a hood. "Hold it closed at your chest level and pull downwards a little, so that the opening is a vertical slit, and see." I did. A vertical world luminous splendor revealed itself to me.

"Breathe into the blanket. Feel that luminosity pulsing around your body?"

"I do, yes."

"Now feel the space between the blanket and your skin. Feel the heat and energy and light radiating off your arms, shoulders, back. Do you feel it?"

"I feel it, grandfather." I could too. It was a thermo cline of heat between me and the cloth. But it tingled too, as if there were little

ynaptic lightning bolts striking out from my skin at the blanket. I
ngled all over like never before.

"Good, feel the pulse of your charged dreamin' body from
ae sun greeting. Feel it, and feel it thicken—that layer between
ou and the blanket. Feel it thicken and strengthen until it is all
round you."

Phillip began to sing in Apache. I sat there seeing an etheric
vorld of glowing incandescence and feeling it envelope and pulse
a, around and through me—and all through the vertical space in
ae slit of the blanket. Then it came to me. I was seeing through
. vertical column of luminosity—and somehow Phillip's singing
trengthened it all.

I began to sing too, or rather hum because I didn't know the
vords. I could feel my diaphragm like a drum reverberating in my
hest. For an unknown time the world disappeared except for us.
Ve sang and the world pulsed luminously in time.

"That was the old song we used to sing to greet the day." He
ɔok the blanket off me. The cool air rushed around me quench-
ag me like a white hot samurai blade dipped in water. He looked
ato the distance as if trying to see back across the ages. He was
ilent for a long time, lost in thought.

"Everyone used to sing that song. There was another for mid-
ay. And one for night." He looked back at me sadly I thought.
Now nobody knows them but me."

"I'll learn them," I said looking up at him, warmth and grati-
ıde spilling out of me.

"Those songs are for the survival of the *Ndee*. They are not
our problem."

"What is my problem, then?"

Phillip shook his head. "Don't worry. Your problems will be
aade plenty clear in time. Right now I want you to stand up
⁄ithout moving."

I exhaled, focused and watched myself stand up inside and
aen outside myself. Then in the next moment, strangely I was see-
ag from a standing position but with that whitish glow of dreaming
ision—then I was again sitting with my eyes closed.

"*Enju shiyee*. That was impeccably done. Now stand up
hysically."

I wobbled to my feet. My left foot had gone to sleep from m
sitting on it. But I wasn't weak like before, just a little dizzy.

"So that's why blankets are so important to Indians—I mea
besides the physical comfort."

Phillip wrapped the blanket around him. He tucked it unde
his right arm thereby leaving his right arm bare. "This is the wa
a warrior wears it. So that his right arm is free to bear weapon:
This is the way a woman wears it."

He wrapped it around his shoulders. "To protect the nursin
babe. Take a look at this." He turned clockwise with his back to me
The blanket was a classic Pendleton so favored by all the India
nations as gifts. A multi-colored, geometric Morningstar patter
overlaid his upper back.

"So the pattern is there to emphasize the seat of the soul?"

"Good question," he replied.

"So what's the answer?" I replied.

"You tell me." Phillip smiled.

"Well, we don't believe in coincidences do we?" I smiled.

"No, we don't," Phillip said.

"Then it's not an accident that the pattern sits right over wher
the soul sits. It's to emphasize it."

"Good. You are answering your own questions as a mar
What else?"

"That cross in the sun. That was wild. That was like Saul-Pat
and Constantine converting to Christianity."

"Yes. That's why we greet the sun that way every day. To rene\
that luminous connection. We used to sing it as well. To return bac
what we had received and complete the hoop and that connectior
That we connect to *Ulsen* the *Bich'ieki'handa'an*, the Life Give
through the living cross of light. Our yellow pollen, *haddentir*
physically represents that light cross, and so we cross ourselve
with it to orient from the physical to the luminosity. That's why w
say 'pollen it is crossed' in our songs and prayers in *Ndee*."

"You're losing me again."

"That's all right, first manhood, then warriorship, then singe:
ship. Just remember these things for later. You'll need 'em."

He pulled the little buckskin bag from under his shirt and undi
it. Then he put his nose to the open mouth of the bag and inhalec

Next he reached inside with his right thumb and index fingers and withdrew a pinch of bright yellow cattail pollen.

"This is a seal upon the power of *Ulsen* that flows into and from us, that we must always use as humble two-leggeds to help others in selfless service to the creator for the creation, and for all our relations."

He made a clockwise circle in front of me and the pollen drifted out of his fingers and to the ground. But coincidentally, or rather not coincidentally I should say, the wind carried it towards my chest.

"See this ceremony so you know why I do this thing," Phillip coached.

I switched almost automatically to luminous sight. I saw the pollen glowing even more brightly and the rays of power extending outward from Phillip's hand. Unlike the pollen, it did not drift down but out, till it interspersed with the luminous glow of my own chest. As it reached my chest, I felt warmth and a tingling where it touched, like a gradual electric current that kept increasing.

"This is what you did before," I realized.

"But now you can see it, and so you understand. This is the beginning of luminous enlightenment. And empowerment comes when you can ride this power, this *diyi*, in selfless service."

"I feel it. Everything you had me do is incredibly empowering, but you're telling me that just looking at the sun I can get all that power? That's pretty hard to swallow. I don't mean any disrespect; I just have a hard time believing."

"No disrespect taken. Your manners are good. Your heart is sincere or you would not be here. A new world has been opened to you, hasn't it, since you learned to see?"

"Yes."

"That was your purification. The dropping of the physical that kept you as a child from experiencing the adult world of power. Now you are learning to empower not only your physical self but your spiritual self as well."

"Right."

"But I am not asking you to believe anything. I am giving you experiences that allow you to test the limits of your sentience, and then choose to move beyond them or not. No man tells another what to do. And I will never tell you what to believe. I will help you have options. But tell me this." He held up that damn brown finger and I got ready.

"How do you empower your physical body?"

I shrugged. "That's easy. You eat healthy and exercise, just like you have me doing."

"And what do you eat?"

"Well, meat and vegetables."

"What do those green plants that you eat, eat themselves?"

"Ah! Sunlight. Photosynthesis. They eat sunlight."

"Oh, that's right. Plants process sunlight. And what about that rabbit, that we ate, what did it eat?"

"Oh! It ate greens too. It ate sunlight. So we're eating processed sunlight! I get it. So that's why yogis are vegetarians. Not to save animals, but to more directly process the energy from the sun."

"No, they also don't want the bad karma associated with the taking of sentient life. But Indians have always made the taking of life in a hunt a form of moving prayer. Just as we did with the rabbit. But we are doing it even more directly than eating greens. We're eating the sunlight directly. This is something all Apaches and most Indians did every day, greeting the sun. It was why they were so strong and so healthy."

"You know, now that I think about it, I was just learning about SAD in biology class last week."

"SAD?"

"Seasonal Affective Disorder, SAD. Millions of people get depressed every winter back East and places where they don't get any real sunlight throughout the winter, you know, like Russia and such."

"Whites always have an acronym for everything, don't they?" Phillip laughed.

"Yeah," I said, happy to be the teacher for a change. "People who don't have access to regular sunlight get irritable; they can't sleep or can't wake up; they get stressed, overeat; they even lose interest in sex."

"So without the light they lose their dreams, and…" he looked at me expectantly.

"Their dreaming bodies! I get it. They lose strength and mass in their dreaming bodies, because they are starving them!"

"And if they're not having sexual connections, as they are not in Russia, what happens to that people as a race?"

"That's right, the birth rate in Russia is dropping. They'll die off as a people; they will become extinct. So we are our own batteries," I said triumphantly.

"*Daha'a, no*. But we don't subscribe to the battery acid school of power. That, as Yoda says, leads to the dark side."

"Dark side."

"Witchcraft. But we'll get to that later. Just remember, we are conductors of *diyi*, not batteries. We are like lasers. We focus God's power through us wherever needed. We don't store it. It is after all not ours. But we'll get to that later. For now focus on what's next."

"Very cool, grandpa. What's next?"

"You practice these techniques until next month, then…"

"We run to the north?"

"We run to the north."

I practiced intensely that month. I could do a hundred pushups and a hundred sit-ups without stopping. I could run two miles in around twelve-and-a-half minutes. I could push out a single mile in around five. I was in incredible shape physically, and my body was ready to move into the further extremes brought on by the spiritual.

I was lean and strong and my legs were like steel springs. I ran between my classes. I ran everywhere. I sat in warrior's seat. It was easy now to become quiet, slow my heart and breath.

In dreaming I could now look at my hands on a regular basis and then move onto other tasks. Sometimes I could stand and even walk—or more accurately kind of glide, in dreaming body. I got to know my bedroom better luminously than physically. And the dorm roof. Every morning at dawn I would do sun greeting from the roof of Mohave dorm. Then I would go downstairs, hit the mall for a jog, and shower afterwards.

My social circle at the U of A had largely given up on me as some kind of weirdo. The drunken parties and dorm rooms of dopers just held no interest for me. I mentioned this to Phillip when I picked him up a month later, but he just shrugged.

"Of course you're losing interest in childish ways: you're becoming a man. That's the whole problem with white society. No manhood and womanhood training, so no more men and women, no more mothers and fathers. The kids have kids and run wild; they grow like weeds, choking themselves and each other off, instead of growing strong and straight like great trees that provide shade and oxygen and fruit. This I think," he looked at me, "will be your task. Head north on Ten."

He reached over me and traced on my chest.

"What's that?"

"See for yourself."

I looked down and clicked in luminous vision. An upside down "S" was just fading away.

"Watch out for that kryptonite now." Phillip smiled broadly.

"Thanks for the tip. Where are we heading?"

"*D'zil T'sa Ts'ian.*"

"Say again, sir."

"In American, Mount Graham, our most sacred site. We are ringed by four great mountain ranges between Arizona and New Mexico, that define the place of the *Ndee* inside the protection of these ranges. From them come our *Ga'an*, our mountain spirits that protect and guide us."

"I heard they were called devil dancers," I ventured.

"An old Catholic missionary term. But they are not that; they are like the Jewish *sephiroth;* they are aspects of *Ulsen,* symptoms of the Creator's existence into the four directions and three dimensions, but of course there are five of them, for the fifth." He held up five fingers for emphasis.

"What's the fifth?"

"*Lubay'ee*, the Gray One, the whirlwind force deity." He traced two opposing lines in the air. "See?" But I was driving and didn't.

"I don't get it."

"It's not important for now. Though it is very important for all Apache. Right now we have a four-hour drive north. I need to tell you about *diyi.*"

"Okay shoot, I mean—" Phillip held up his hand. He was very serious.

"Remember last when we were talking about batteries and lasers?"

"Yes, sir."

"Never forget it or this. This is why many Christians and good religious people call me a witch doctor or think the *Ga'an* are dancing with the devil. Because we do deal with power. They are afraid of *diyi*, just like they are afraid of a gun or a knife or any kind of power. The Maya so feared the mountain *Ga'an* that they sacrificed their own maiden, virgin daughters to them. To be sure they honored them and painted them and even drugged them so that they would feel no pain. But they still sacrificed them like slaves. The same way white slavers do today with our little girls for the sex trade."

He tapped me sharply enough on the shoulder so that it stung. I looked over at him. His eyes were sharp and shining with an inner light of intensity.

"But we are Apache. A race of pure warriors. Born of Slayer of Enemies. Free-est of the free. We do not sacrifice our children. We bow to no man and no spirit. We pray standing but with humble respect—and only to the One God. We ride the spiritual force of the *Ga'an* like bull riders in rodeo, to bless our maidens in the Sunrise ceremony. We have never submitted to any spirit, evil or good. We are the true, free Red Clay people descended from the *Adamas*, children of *Iz'landelehe'e,* the White Painted One, the Lady. Don't ever forget that. And don't ever bow down and break your connection."

"Yes, sir." I was unsure of understanding all that I heard but that was nothing new. The intensity of the message however was unmistakable. I filed it away for later use. And it would be only after many years later that I would understand the enormity of the statement, the significance of the moment, and the true human bravery of its meaning.

"We are warriors, protectors of children and women; we place ourselves between innocence and evil. We choose God and good and reject bad and evil, and we fight against evil, everywhere and always! But as warriors we do not fear guns or knives or battle. We know battle and the weapons of battle, spiritually and physically, just as you have learned with these."

He held up a bone-handled knife in a rawhide sheath in one hand and buckskin encased mace-like war club in the other.

"Except you used newspaper and socks for your training, instead of the real thing. Here." He handed me the knife, sheathed, handle first. I took my right hand off the wheel and took the handle in my hand. Abruptly Phillip pulled back on the sheath, drawing the knife for me. I quickly pointed the blade away from Phillip and myself.

"Scared?" Phillip asked.

"Nope," I replied hefting the knife. It was old but elegant, and obviously deadly.

"What about this?" He held up an arrow.

"Nope."

"Why not?"

"Because...I have been trained to understand its meaning and its use."

"Good. It is the same way with all power, guns, or pure energy *diyi*. But the non-warrior who see us use *diyi*, even in selfless service, fear it and us and call us witches and devil dancers. Just like the city folks that are afraid of guns and therefore want to disempower everyone else to their level of helplessness. Do you understand the difference?"

"I think so. It's the Christian prohibition on seers and soothsayers and channeling—using spirits for personal benefit. And personal transformation by spiritual manipulation of these spiritual forces."

"Yes, we are changed by our training. But the purpose of our training is to become better conductors of *diyi*, not collectors of it, and never for ourselves, always for others." I was silent for a while and so was Phillip. "Many folks are afraid of us because of our ability to use power, and you know what?"

"What?" I bit.

"They are right, absolutely. What we do is extremely dangerous. Never forget that."

"Yes, sir."

"Now pay close attention. Never forget and always remember this. There are two schools of power. One is the battery acid school. You can take power and store it up." Then he held up a small Duracell C-sized battery.

"When Apaches would take a prisoner in the old days and torture him to death, building a fire between his legs or staking him out on an anthill and rubbing Mescal juice on his head for the ants to eat, or rape, these are all examples of taking *diyi*, of instilling terror as one dies to close off the soul and damage it, and to take that leaking luminance and hold it. That's why some Indians scalped, to hold that luminescence, to hold an enemy's spirit, after you have taken his life. This is even the way warfare is called in the ancient Chiricauhua battle language."

He shifted towards me in his seat. "All bad things that men do to each other are really designed in the end to take their power. To warm themselves from the heat off the flame of their soul. We have done these things as have all men. But they are wrong and we were wrong to do them, as the soldiers were wrong to do them to our women and children...as men still do all over the world to each other."

We drove on in silence for a while. He seemed lost in mourning for the uncounted wrongs done to his people. Then I spoke.

"*Shiwoye*, what is the other way?" He didn't answer right away. He was still remembering, and recounting wrongs done in his mind, or so I thought.

"*Shiwoye*."

Something was clearly bothering him. "Anyway, the other way is our way. And for us it is the only way. It is the crystal school of empowerment. Apaches often use crystal to help them see, and to focus *diyi* to heal or strike like lasers."

He pulled a small crystal out of his pocket, held it up and squinted through it. "So become like a crystal, to act like a laser, become more clear, more transparent, drop more ego and you will be able to reflect *Ulsen's diyi* anywhere you need to—to focus it like a laser to cut out a cancer—or warm a heart. That," he said, "is the only way to use power."

He placed his hand on my shoulder. "Always remember this simple formula, and no matter what kind of power you access for whatever purpose for good, you will be all right. Listening?"

"All ears, sir."

"Power plus ego always equals evil. Repeat it," he commanded.

"Power plus ego always equals evil," I said.

"That means if you ever use power for yourself, for selfish purposes, no matter how small or insignificant, then you are doing witchcraft and you are a witch."

"Seems kind of harsh."

"It is the razor edge between good and evil. Never cross it."

"What about like love magic, like I've heard they do on the rez."

"Especially love magic and especially on the reservation. We're here. Pull off to the right here. We'll do sun greeting and then run."

We both turned and faced the sun. I slowly mirrored Phillip's movements and felt the familiar heat and energy shoot up my groin along my spine and out the top of my crown. When we finished, Phillip turned in a clockwise circle.

"Turn in a circle. This is an Apache 'amen,' like the movement of the sun—and something else, do you know what?"

"What, *shiwoye*."

"A man figures out answers for himself. Drink and hold." He handed me the cup. I took it without hesitation, drinking but not swallowing.

His bright smile flashed in the dawn's rays. "Just like this blessing." He made a clockwise circle then moved his hand through it west to east, then north to south, just this time with no pollen.

"There is a history lesson for you—of mankind, right there in the movement of my hand. You see the world, then the great disconnection of heaven to earth, and then the final vertical line upwards—to the great reconnection."

As I puzzled over the gravity of his last comments, he turned abruptly and took off running. I shook my head free of my lingering musings and followed, feeling light and strong.

"See," he called over his shoulder, and I did.

Mount Graham was high altitude and covered in Ponderosa pine. It was cold and foggy and Phillip nearly disappeared into the mist except for the glow of his luminosity. I ran easily bursting with power, leaping gracefully over streams and boulders like a deer. I had never felt so strong and happy. We covered several miles. This was a major mountain range. The biggest yet. There was no end in sight, but I was confident that after my many months of hard training I could keep up.

"See the trees and the branches," Phillip called out.

As luminous vision kicked in, every blade of grass and pebble glowed and pulsed, as did I as I passed. I began to see even more clearly and focused on the trees. I couldn't see the tree tops near but in the distance I watched their glow. I quickly noticed that their halos did not stop at their tops but continued up and into the sky fading into the sunlight!

I looked at the low growing branches of the pines and chaparral near me. They too extended a luminous glow beyond their physical counterparts.

"Extend your fingers alongside your belly." Phillip whispered hoarsely.

He was suddenly alongside me, and he was breathing heavily. I think the attitude was finally getting to him. "See from your fingertips too."

I placed my fingertips alongside my belly and extended them outwards. Almost immediately I saw lines of power extend from my fingertips. Then surprisingly I saw lines in front of me, touching my finger lines. Some of the lines arced out from the nearby chaparral and tree branches. Others just disappeared into the mist. I couldn't see where they came from. The lines arced out and briefly touched my fingers, and then my stomach and chest, like little synaptic bursts, as I passed. I could feel my energy level increasing even as I physically tired. It was as if I was being charged by every living tree I passed. It was a strange sensation to actually have more energy, even though I could feel myself physically fade. As my luminosity engaged and interacted with these lines, I could feel my body being pulled along by these lines, actually increasing my pace, even though I had run much farther than ever before. My legs struggled to keep up with my spirit.

Abruptly Phillip turned and struck at me. I turned to the right just in time to avoid his strike, and then somehow he struck again. He stood there grinning crazily at me.

"How did you do that?"

"What?"

"Strike twice like that, move twice?"

He shook his head slowly and shook gently with quiet laughter.

"What's so funny?" I asked, putting my hands on my hips and crossing my legs to stretch them. "I just don't see how you could move like that."

"That," he said, when he stopped laughing, "is exactly what you saw."

"Huh?"

"It's not me, it's you. Your sight." He laughed again. "That's why it's called second sight."

I stood there a moment. Then it slowly dawned on me.

"You mean, I first saw your dreaming body strike, then your physical followed."

Phillip nodded happily. "Well done. *Ugash.*"

He turned on his heel and ran off. I followed, now shaking my head. I had seen Phillip's dreaming body move ahead of his physical. We went on for miles and hours. I don't know how far. The sun went from low to overhead to low. The mountain stretched on endlessly. We never reached the top. But finally the trailed circled downwards again. Eventually I stopped seeing and just became on automatic pilot, gliding along the lines.

My world closed around me in exhaustion. We ran on and on until time and space lost all meaning. I looked ahead at Phillip's much older form steadily trotting ahead of me in the famous endless Apache trot. Even though I was tired, I vowed not to quit Phillip's mute form moving out in front of me was motivation enough. Finally we completed a long, clockwise circle around the mountain and stopped very near the car. We both took long drinks and leaned against the hood.

"Heck of a run," I panted.

"Not bad," he replied. "In the old days we could even run down deer. The Tarahumara in Mexico, they still run hundreds of miles in only hours, and straight up and down the Sierra Madres in Mexico, kicking a little wooden ball, playing the game for days at a time."

"Guess I'm lucky you're not Mexican Indian," I grinned.

"Guess so. How about building a fire over there in that clearing *shiye'e*," Phillip said.

I nodded and staggered off. I wandered around recovering standing dead wood and piling it up next to an old fire pit already ringed with stones. In short order I had a good fire roaring. Phillip limped over. Steam still rose from both of us.

"*Enju.* Now go pile those rocks up over there, sixteen high." He threw a small stone about fifteen feet away.

I got up and groaned. I was sore and stiff and totally spent. I splashed through a nearby puddle and stumbled over an unstable rock. Now that I had stopped running, the endorphins had fled and the lines were gone. I was dead tired and completely exhausted. Even my fingers were stiff. The rocks were cold and hard in my hands. The rocks were grapefruit to basketball size. I slowly began piling them up vertically.

"How's that?" I called to him. I had the rocks knee high. The sun was setting early on the far side of the mountain and darkness was fast approaching. Phillip sat warming himself by the fire.

"Higher," he yelled back.

"Was afraid you'd say that," I said. "How high?"

"To your chest. Build with four on the base then four up, then three and three, then two-two, then four ones on top of each other."

"Got it," I said. I finished the design quickly now that I had a plan to follow.

I wobbled back over to the fire and sat down. Phillip handed me the same blanket as before. He pointed with his chin for me to wrap in it. I did so gratefully. "What's the point?" I pointed my chin at the rock pile, just visible in the gathering darkness.

"In the old days we used to build altars like that out in the mountains just like the Israelites. Sometimes when you are way out in the wild, you'll still come across them, like at *besh ba gowa.*"

"The stone houses," I translated out loud. "So what does it do?"

"A demonstration of *Ulsen's diyi*," Phillip said gravely. "I show this to you now, not for myself, not for pride, but so that you will know, that when you need *diyi*, in selfless service, you will be worthy—and ready." He stood up and faced out from the fire.

"Is lightning going to strike that rock tower or what?" I joked. Phillip ignored me as if he had never even heard me. He faced the rocks. Slowly, almost imperceptibly he raised his right arm palm down, index finger pointed.

"See," he commanded in an authoritative voice.

I relaxed my gaze. It was only seconds by the time my second sight shifted in, but there was already a long luminous line—like a laser arrow emerging straight from Phillip's finger. His frame glowed an electric blue. I watched it extend into the darkness. The rocks were now just outside of the firelight.

In the next instant I heard the rock tower tumble noisily downwards upon itself!

Although I did not see the rocks fall, I heard them and I can hear them today, some thirty years later. I bolted to my feet, stumbled and fell backwards. I crawled backwards like a scalded crab, then stopped. I was too stunned to speak. What I had just heard was miraculous and terrifyingly powerful.

Phillip's face was a grim mask of burnished copper in the firelight. My mouth hung open. I literally could not form words to respond to what I had just witnessed. I stared into the darkness, in the direction of the rocks. Luminous vision seemingly of its own volition kicked in and Phillip, the rocks and the trees glowed twice, first in the gold of the firelight, then in the clearer shining of their electromagnetic pulse. Little bubbles of incandescence shimmered and bobbed behind Phillip amongst the trees.

"*Twerdums*," he said, "those are the ghosts of the little people."

"What?" I whispered. Suddenly the night was a very scary place indeed, full of the unknown and the unexplainable.

"Want to go see?" Phillip said softly. His eyes glistened in the firelight.

"No, sir," I whispered. "I'm just fine, right here."

The enormity of what I had just witnessed weighed down upon me like an alien gravity. But evidently Phillip wasn't finished.

"Stand," he ordered. I was on my feet before I knew it. "Slap me on the left arm."

I gathered my courage and stepped in and swung in gently, to my surprise and relief, tapping him on his left, upper arm.

"Again, but hard this time." I nodded and stepped in, pivoted and slapped him harder this time.

"Better, but not hard enough. This time as hard as you can. Go."

I stepped in and pivoted fast. My elbow led my arm. My hand followed.

"Why did you stop?"

"What?" I had stopped in mid-strike and mid-step. I lowered my hand.

"What happened?"

"You tell me."

"I, I went to slap you...and, I don't know, it's like my mind just blinked."

"Yes, that's a good way to put it. You know that when you hunt, and you fire your rifle, your ears blink, and after the shot, they don't ring. The same thing happens in combat. But if you go to the range and fire with ear plugs—they'll ring. Now push me."

"Huh?"

"How much do you weigh?"

"Maybe one eighty-five."

"Good, I'm one sixty, if that, and thirty-some years older. Push me as hard as you can, straight back. Do it now."

Afraid to and afraid not to I pushed against him, grabbing with both arms and leaning deeply forward. My feet slid backwards on the rocks.

"Come on. You can do better than that," he whispered into my ears. "Push now, hard as you can."

I strained against him but it was no use.

"It's like pushing at a tree," I panted.

"Yup. Lots of people wonder why Cochise was named after fire and a tree. This is partly why. He was immovable as a rooted Oak. In the old days we were great wrestlers from boyhood to manhood. But no one could move him. He never lost. Want to know about the *ko*, the fire part?"

I still strained against him while he just stood there completely relaxed. But now suddenly he walked forward driving me like I wasn't even there. I finally lost my footing over a fallen sycamore trunk and went down on my rear. I lay there physically spent and still emotionally stunned.

"No, sir. I believe I'll pass for tonight."

He stepped back to the fire and pulled a black-tipped, white eagle feather from a piece of rolled up rawhide in the back waist of his jacket. It had a piece of turquoise tied to it from a long, buckskin cord. He went to a nearby tree limb and tied it there, at head height, leaving it hanging free. The feather briefly twisted and then became still.

"Your turn."

"Huh?"

"Reach out and send a line of luminosity out to the *itsaa.*"

"Okay."

I extended my right arm and right index finger, knit my eye brows and thought about the feather moving.

"No, no, that's not what I taught you. Stop thinking. Breathe."

I took a deep breath.

"Relax. See and just watch it happen."

I started again. I raised my hand and pointed my finger. And then, I relaxed, and watched wondrously as a fuzzy funnel slowly merged, faltered and then renewed itself outwards slowly, ponderously out until finally it reached the eagle feather. Just then, a wind came up and whipped the remains of the fire, showering sparks The feather whipped on the cord.

"*Enju*," Phillip intoned. "Sit on down." He sat back down by the fire.

"But I think the wind moved it," I protested.

Phillip waived his hand. "So?"

"But I'd like to try again."

"That's enough for today. You did fine. Untie the *itsa'a*."

"But," I protested, "how do I know that I moved the feather separate from the wind?"

Phillip shook his head and rolled his eyes. "You don't. And you're missin' the point."

"How so?" I went to untie the feather.

"You didn't do anything separate from anything, including the wind. You did it with *diyi* and with the wind, which is also *diyi*."

"But how will I ever know what I can do alone."

"You won't. Have you forgotten everything I have taught you?"

"No, sir."

"Because you do nothing alone. *Diyi* only flows through you. Mother Teresa said she is a good little pencil for God to write with. Fools Crow said he is a good, hollow bone for *Wakan Tanka* to flow through."

"But in a crisis, how will I know?"

Phillip ambled off towards the car. "You know, that's the funny thing. You never know. You just have to take the chance. Every time."

I stamped out the fire in a flurry of sparks and a plume of smoke, and then walked to the car. Phillip looked over the hood at me.

"Wanna know something else?" Our gazes locked.

"What?"

"I'm surprised every time. Every time. That," he nodded, "is why it works." He got into the car.

I looked up at the starry sky. The Milky Way spilled out its stars like diamonds in a wide, bright belt across the high perigee of the night sky. A falling star streaked across the sky burning up as it hit the atmosphere and briefly brightening the sky. I nodded to myself. I remembered reading about Tecumseh's birth, and the comet called the Panther's Eye that had passed over the sky that night.

I climbed in the car, cranked the engine and turned on the lights. The brilliant magic of the night disappeared in the tiny, narrow beams.

*"There is a history lesson for you—of mankind
right there in the movement of my hand.
You see the world, then the great disconnection
of heaven to earth and then the final vertical line
upwards—to the great reconnection."*

Gotta get up at dawn for this one. Even better if you run first. Pre-position your blanket.

Face the rising sun, hands over groin.

Put your hands just off and over your groin, thumb almost touching, index fingers pointing down and almost touching as well.

Feel a pulse of energy and heat between your thumbs, fingers, and radiating between your palms and groin.

Inhale deeply and slowly raise your arms to the rising sun.

Squint as sunshine rays spill into you.

Move your eyes and head from right to left, but as the sun rises, don't look directly at it; it will just blind you.

Raise your hands to the sun, just blocking the orb itself with your fingertips.

Place your thumb and index finger just touching, forming your own Morningstar eclipse.

A shining, white light cross should appear.

Feel the warmth of the sun on your palms and fingertips.

Filter the rays of the shining cross into the pupils of your eyes.

Now let your fingers and hands spread apart.

See.

Now come slowly down along your sides, exhaling as you go, until your fingers reunite again just over your groin.

Now sit in warrior seat. Keep your back straight. Chin tucked. Tongue on the roof of your mouth.

Drape your blanket over your head and torso, like a hood.

Hold it closed at your chest level and pull downwards a little so that the opening is a vertical slit.

See.

Breathe into the blanket.

Feel luminosity pulsing around your body.

Feel the space between the blanket and your skin.

Feel the heat and energy and light radiating off your arms, shoulders, back.

Feel it thicken—that layer between you and the blanket.

Feel it thicken and strengthen until it is all around you.

NATURAL LAW

The Apaches emphasized the life on earth through rites and ceremonies.... They emphasized good behavior.... It was not a matter of future punishment, but of doing what was right because it was right.

—Dan Nicholas

"*Handa,*" Phillip's voice wafted out from behind the screen door. My hand was poised to knock.

"How do you do that?" I pulled the door open and stepped in confidently and comfortably.

"Come on in, *shiyee.* When you know how, you'll be able to do it too."

I stepped into the room. I was lean, bronze and muscled from my months of training, eager for the next phase and ready for anything. I was even wearing my moccasins.

"So what's it going to be today, grandpa, a run, the bow, how about a sweat? I'm ready for any of 'em, or all of 'em."

Phillip lay back on the battered sofa. He had his feet up on a flimsy coffee table.

"Sit on down. We're gonna watch TV." He patted the couch cushion next to him.

"TV?" I sat down, but on the floor, my back against the couch. As usual he had surprised me again and as always in a totally unexpected way.

"So how did you like your first run ceremony?"

"I didn't know there was such a thing."

"There is now."

Just then a knock came on the screen door.

"Phil, you in there?" an old man's voice called from the door.

"Phil?" I looked at him. He put his finger to his lips and winked.

"I am, George, come on in," Phillip yelled back. "And that was a long time ago. But now you have run in the four directions to own the four ages of your life. Don't you feel stronger and better prepared in all ways for your hard life as a man?"

"I do, grandfather." He nodded and the screen door creaked open.

"This your grandson, Phil?" An older man, in Coke bottle glasses, gaunt and gray, stepped into the room. He was shabbily dressed and obviously ground down by life.

"Yup, George, this is Jeffrey, my grandson." Phillip waived a hand in my direction and then at George and I felt a surge of warmth rush over my abdomen. I stood up and extended my hand.

"Nice to meet you, sir." He took my hand. It was cool and weak.

"Good to meet you too, Jeffrey." He squinted at me, then Phillip. "You adopted or something? You don't look Indian."

"I...."

"He is," Phillip chimed in.

"Well, that's great; had a cousin once that was adopted, but didn't work out; they sent him back when he was about fourteen, back in sixty-two, sixty-three maybe," he said.

"Well, we're keeping him; we work him too hard to send him back," Phillip said amiably.

"So I'm adopted?" I looked back at Phillip.

"Adopted and apprenticed." Phillip made a circle and cross sign with his right hand in my general direction. "Twice double— for the trouble."

"Well, that's great—too many abortions today. Hey, listen Phil," George turned excitedly to Phillip. "She's finally sleeping so I'm going to go see Cecilia, watch the *Price Is Right* over a her place. If Lil wakes up, you just tell her you sent me on some errands to fix your faucet, okay?"

"Okay, George, I'll tell her. But when are you goin' to fix my faucet?"

George was already half way out the door. He turned back and whispered "Well, I'll get on that today, Phil, I promise, but right now I gotta get going."

"Hey, George," Phillip whispered back.

George was already out the door, but he stopped and stuck his head back in.

"Yeah, Phil?"

"Say hi to you-know-who for me."

"Will do, amigo, will do." He winked and was gone.

"What was that all about?" I asked.

"That was George, my landlord. He lives in the duplex next door with his wife Lilly."

"Then who's Cecilia?"

"That's his girl, so to speak, although she must be sixty if she's a day. Well now, life has impeccable timing, doesn't it? So what about that? Old George has a lady friend on the side. What do you think about that?" Phillip looked at me, his eyes shining with humor.

"I guess that's wrong. It's immoral, I mean."

"That's right. According to the word of the book from the Moses tablets, thou shalt not covet thy neighbor's wife."

"The ten commandments."

"Exactly, they're pretty much the same for the three desert-mountain tribes, Jew, Christian and Muslim. And they are a good law, know why?"

"Why?"

"Because the word says that it is too great a wrong to bear and to forgive. Makes sense right?"

"Sure."

"But now George here, he's been married to Lilly upwards fifty years maybe and…"

"You talking about me, dirty old redskin," a raspy, hoarse voice that grated like sandpaper drifted through the screen door along with the odor of stale cigarette smoke—and something else even more unpleasant. "Get out here where I can see you."

Phillip grimaced, then turned to me, winked and rose. He walked over to the door and opened it a crack. I leaned forward to see over his shoulder.

A monstrous old woman with rolls of fat hanging from her everywhere leaned heavily on an aluminum walker. A cigarette dangled from her lip, the long ash threatening to fall off and ignite her enormous belly at any moment. She was nearly bald and in several spots, as I looked closer, I realized she actually was. Her moo-moo was filthy and as she moved closer, I realized she stank.

"Where is that worthless pair of empty pants?" she huffed.

"And who would that be, Lilith?" Phillip said soothingly.

"Don't you dare sass a white woman. You know who I'm talking about, you red nigger. Where is he?" She sputtered, and spittle actually flew onto the screen door.

"Not here. He went to Ace to get some stuff to fix my faucet."

"Ace, well how stupid! Why didn't he just go to Jenson's? It's only two blocks away."

"Because I asked him to get the good joint connectors. That leak just keeps coming back."

I laughed to myself. I had used that faucet several times and it did leak. Phillip glanced at me with mock anger.

"Who you got in there with you? You got a girl in there?"

"No, Lil."

"Don't you lie to me. I heard somebody laughing in there. You got a girl you grabbed in there." She stopped ranting as she was enveloped in a fit of coughing that racked her frame. She momentarily removed her cigarette in two yellowed fingers and spit straight down onto Phillip's welcome mat. "You're lying, boy!"

"It's not a girl, Lil," Phillip paused for dramatic effect, "It's a boy!"

Lilith's mouth fell open. Her eyes widened under her bags. Somehow the cigarette stuck to her greasy lower lip. "That's it, I'm calling the cops, right now too. You're going to jail or the grave today, Mr. Tonto Kimosabe, that's right!"

She ambled off, her walker clicking in time to her continuous flow of rambling and raving.

Phillip grimaced and shook his head sadly. Then his gaze fixed on something outside. He opened the screen door and raised his right arm straight out and pointed in a sharp, quick motion.

I rose too and moved closer to see what he was targeting. Just as I stepped into the door's view I heard a clanging "CAAW"! A huge black crow flapped noisily off a low limb on the mesquite tree out back. The bird had been so unusually close that I felt the air forced by its wings. Phillip followed the flight of the crow till it was out of sight.

"Weird," I said.

"Hmm?" Phillip said in a distracted voice.

"I said that was weird that crow was so close. What a weird coincidence."

"Did you see it?" he asked.

"Yeah, it was the biggest crow I've ever seen."

"No. Did you *see* it?"

"Oh no, sorry, grandfather, it was too quick."

"Hmm, too bad. There are no coincidences. None. Ever. Remember that. But Lil was a show unto herself, wasn't she?"

We walked back inside and sat down. I shook my head. "I can't believe you put up with that."

"Guess I could have taken a stick to her like we did to our women in the old days, or better yet, shot the crow. But neither of those actions would deal with the source of the problem."

"Which is?"

"Exactly the right question." He slapped my leg. "Good boy. But back to the subject at hand which is manhood, specifically impeccability, not warriorship, not yet."

"Ah, what's that mean?"

"It means like the man said that jumped out of the burning airplane, 'One thing at a time, one thing at a time.'" He grinned. "So you were telling me that George is immoral, right?"

"Okay, I think I see where you are going here. But why doesn't he just divorce her?"

"He takes care of her. She needs a lot of care, even though she won't take care of herself."

"Is that his problem?"

"He thinks it is. But you know about a year ago, he came over here in tears. Said he couldn't take the abuse anymore, that he was just going to kill himself. He got out an old six-gun and was shakin' so bad he could hardly load it."

"What happened?"

"Well, that's the funny thing. A lady reporter from the *Star* came over that day to interview me on the Sunrise ceremony. George, he stopped in and they just hit it off. Never seen him so happy. Guess it's just a great big coincidence."

"Wait a minute, *shiwoye*, I thought you said there are no coincidences."

"Ah, so you are paying attention."

"Of course I'm paying attention. But I don't get the point."

"The point is this," he leaned forward and raised that long, brown finger, "if without Cecelia, George would have killed himself, then who would there be to care for Lilly?"

"Nobody. I'm sure nobody else would put up with that shit."

"So should he have done the moral thing and remained faithful to a woman that had neither faith nor love for him—even though that choice would have driven him to suicide? Or should he have done what he needed to survive and maintain some happiness and self-esteem for himself, something that he got none of at home, so that he could continue to care for Lil?"

"I see your point." I nodded. "And life is complicated when you are an adult."

"We spoke earlier about the book people, Talmud and Testament, and their most important commandment words. But the Apache had no such commandments, and those commandments are the basis for American law, lawmen and judges—even soldiers. But the Apache and the other Indian peoples did not need police and laws. They just did what was right, in the right place, and at the right time. That," he looked at me, "is impeccable, natural, law."

"But what about the new word and the new book, the new testament?"

"That book is about *Naya'es'kane'e,* in *Ndee,* Slayer of Monsters, in Hebrew, *Yeshua*, in English it is Jesus. Very good point

And what did Jesus say when the Pharisees asked him if they should, according to their law, stone the adulteress?"

I thought for a long moment. "Um, forgive her?"

"*Ow*, yes."

"He said, 'Let he who is without sin cast the first stone.' Now that was not the legal, lawful, moral answer according to Jewish law—but it was the impeccable one, according to natural law, because it allowed Christianity to move beyond the blood feuds that still engulf the Mid-east."

"Course," he said with a wink, "there was that one chunk of concrete came flyin' in from the back of the crowd and hit her in the head. Then Yeshua there, he got up on his toes, looked back into the crowd and said—'MOM'!"

He smiled and I laughed. "And when the Pharisee legal eagles questioned him about the law, what did he say?"

"What?" I asked.

"I give you a new law, to replace the others. Love God, love one another with your whole heart. And there was nothing in there about just platonically or heterosexually. Just love. What can be more impeccable and natural and divine, than that, to act out of love always?"

"What about combat and war?"

"You been to war?"

"No, sir."

"I have. Did you know that there are Indian warrior societies that one cannot join unless one has been to war? Soldiers act out of love for the guy on their right and left. Not out of hate. Guys don't fall on grenades out of hate...."

His voice trailed off and his eyes got a long, distant look to them as if he was looking back to another time and place, perhaps some frozen foreign battlefield. "They do it out of love for their buddies. Sometimes buddies they don't even like, but they love. That's why a guy out of nowhere just lays on a grenade. Love." Phillip was lost for a moment to the battlefields of his past, too awful to talk about. Then he said, "Uh, where was I?"

"Jesus."

"Ah yes, Jeee-sus." He drew it out like a television evangelist.

"They hated him for workin' on the Sabbath. Daring to heal the sick on their day off. Just like they killed us for dancing—and dreamin'. Nothing scares bureaucrats more than spiritual power. It's something they can't control, they can't buy off. When the drums start, pretty soon they start shooting us."

"So you are saying that Jesus was immoral but impeccable?"

"How else can you explain the contradictions? One day he tells his apostles to all go buy two swords each—he's a warrior, and of course he's always fighting demons. But when he's not, he's healing the sick; he's a healer. And he says, he who lives by the sword dies by the sword. Then the next thing you know, he puts an ear back on and says who lives by the sword dies by it."

"Just like the Apache did. You're saying they did the naturally right thing without rules and laws."

"*Ow*—yes. Because they followed natural law, they were impeccably balanced between physical and spiritual to be a whole human being."

"Ah, so that's why all the Indians call themselves the human beings and the others half-alive, or half-asleep. Because they're not balanced."

"How can they be balanced when they have no spiritual side and no spiritual training? Their dreaming body just flops around in their nightmares like some landed trout."

"So how do you know if you are following natural law?" I asked.

"Simple. Are you connecting or disconnecting?"

"To what, or from what?"

"Yes, exactly?"

"Huh?"

"Huh what?" Phillip laughed. I felt like I was in some kind of Abbot and Costello who's-on-first skit.

"I'll put it another way. There was this preacher down south in the bayou. And a big flood came. His parishioners asked him to leave with them in their car. But he said, 'No, God will provide.' Then those waters came up inside the church. And he was standing up on the pews when this Red Cross boat comes by and they say, 'Get in, padre.' But he says, 'Nope, God'll provide.' Then those flood waters, just like with *Island'ele'he'e* in the abalone, they came all the way up." Phillip stood up and started acting out the story.

"So he's up on the roof now of the church, clingin' to the spire and cross, and a national guard helicopter comes down and hovers and says, 'Hop on, preacher.' But he just shakes his head and says 'Nope, me and Jesus are like this.' He held up two crossed fingers.

"God'll take care of me. I got faith. Well, those waters kept on comin' and he drowns. And he goes up to those pearly gates and he says to the Lord, 'Hey, I believed in you. Why didn't you come rescue me?' And the Lord's voice booms back, 'I gave you three chances.'"

We laughed together for a moment. For a serious and intense young man, it was a sterling moment, just sitting on that couch and sharing a good laugh with Phillip. This was hardly the stereotype of the stoic and deadly Apache warrior that I had expected. Phillip was always teaching me and always making me laugh. Thirty years later it is a lesson I am only now starting to fully appreciate.

"Now," he paced back and forth in front of the couch, "the standard for impeccable, natural law is whether your actions are connecting or disconnecting you to the hoop and the web, continuing to increase *shita'kee*, connections to others."

"Web, what web?" I asked.

"Go to that back kitchen window. Look out into the clearing." I got up and made my way to the window. In between the big, white cottonwoods with their pale green leaves, the gold grass of the clearing and the sweat lodge was partially visible.

"Okay, now what?"

"Now see the air in between the clearing."

I refocused into soft, peripheral luminous vision. After a moment the luminosity of the trees and bushes popped into view. Now that I was looking or rather seeing, I noticed that the limbs and branches didn't go just up, but out, and in every direction and in some cases, even down.

"Got it," I said.

"Good, now look at the space in between, in the clearing. See the lines of luminosity around the tree limbs and branches?"

"Yes sir, I do."

"Now follow those out, where do they go?"

I relaxed my vision even more and followed the luminous lines fading off and out into the air.

"Got it?"

"Got it, sir."

"Where do those lines go?"

"Everywhere. They follow the directions of the branches and limbs."

"So where do they go to?"

"Uh," I looked out again more carefully, "they just keep going out in the direction the physical limb went...they just sort of fade out in the same direction."

"So do some of those lines cross?" Phillip prodded. I looked more. Yep, sure enough, the bushes near each other showed luminous crossings, so did the trees.

"Yes sir, they sure do. And so do the tree limbs and even some of the trunks," I called over my shoulder.

"Hmm. Now you see anything else out there that has crossed lines."

I was staring straight out at the willow lodge. The shaved limbs glowed almost the same soft yellowish tint of the luminosity coming off them. They were crossed, just like the overlapping branches, and their corresponding luminosity.

"The lodge, it's crossed, just like the limbs and just like the luminosity. And," I turned back to face him, "just like our interlocking obligations of *shita'kee* to each other. We are defined by our obligations, our duties to others." I smiled at the subtlety of Phillip's guidance and the sublime truths his elegant leadership had brought to me.

"Acting impeccably, following natural law on the right luminous crossed line, or uncrossed line, and at the right time...that,' Phillip smiled back, "is following the trail of natural law."

"See, I remember our first talk out there." I pressed my finger against the window pane.

"Glad you do. I can't remember anything anymore. You remember, remember it all. Because somewhere down the line you're goin' to need it."

"You know, you are always so reassuring." I turned to Philip.

"Come on back in here and sit down. It's almost on."

"What?"

"What we're gonna watch." I slowly sat down on the floor facing the TV, my back against the couch.

"We're really going to just watch TV?" I said, amazed that anything with him could be so easy.

"Soon, it's a movie about Apache."

"That's funny, my dad, he pulled me out of school when I was in the seventh grade to watch Burt Lancaster in *Apache.* Is that the movie we're watching?"

"No, but I remember it. That was about a bronco *Ned'ni* Apache named Massai. There's a peak named after him up north. No, this one's different." He glanced at a TV guide and then a pocket watch, both on the table next to the sofa. "We got a little more time. I want to talk to you about rules. Rules, not laws, mind you. All Indian nations were warrior societies. And the greatest of these was the Apache. We were a pure warrior culture." He stood up and was suddenly very tall, intimidating and even dangerous looking.

"We took this land from the Zuni and Hopi and held it. With *hash'ka'le.* It means fierceness. Apache comes from the Zuni word *Apachu,* meanin' enemy. We raided every one around us. Stole their horses, their grain, and their women. And the Mexicans, we killed them with rocks, not to waste bullets. But our most sacred ceremony is the Sunrise, about a maiden, a virgin girl child coming of age."

"I remember, you told me."

"There are two great rules that defined all the Indian warrior societies. I want you to remember them." He held up two fingers.

"The first is this: Nothing must ever be done to harm the children." He pointed to an Apache painting on the wall that showed an Apache Madonna and child.

A beautiful young Apache woman in a white buckskin dress knelt with her hands at the sides of her head facing us, as if she was dancing from that kneeling position. From her flowed a waterfall and below was a baby Apache boy over the water. Before I had thought it was Mary and Jesus done Apache style. But now I realized it was White Painted Lady and Child Born of Water.

"This is by a *Yavapai* Apache friend of mine named Duke Sine. It visually encapsulates and sums up our spiritual traditions and beliefs."

"It's beautiful," I said. And it was. But he wasn't finished.

"The second great rule is this: Everything is born of woman."

He brought a basket down off the wall and hugged it to his chest. He took a conical Apache basket with fringe hanging down and tin cones on the fringe, off the wall. As he moved it, the cones jingled in a pleasant way. He turned it upside down and held it over his groin.

"It's shaped like a woman's womb." He shook it. The cones jingled again pleasantly.

"That's the sound of woman. Of home and civilization. This is a *tatsa*. It's called a burden basket. The women would put a wide buckskin band here called a tumpline. Wear it on their forehead, and the *tatsa* would hang on their back like this." He put it on to demonstrate.

"Then they would gather berries and, as they picked the berries, they would just drop them in back there. Sometime the bears would be in that same berry patch and those women would fight off those bears. One woman, she killed that bear with her camp knife, then she tied her scalp back on—that a big black bear had torn off—picked up her berry basket and went on home. When folks ask me how tough Apache men are, I say, you should see our women."

He smiled and sat back down passing me the basket. I looked inside. Its weave started in the bottom center with a circled cross in woven cat's claw and willow. In the bottom were several kernels of varied colored corn.

"Remember *2001: A Space Odessy?*"

"Sure do. I was in the eighth grade when it came out. Great movie."

"Well, you remember that scene where the missing-link ape man, he figures out how to use that tapir's hip bone as a weapon? And then the tribe is all fed by eating meat from his kill."

"I do."

"Well, that's all wrong." Civilization began with the women gathering edible wild vegetation. Hunting was a dangerous, time-consuming gamble. Besides, first men just scavenged from predator kills. Women did the real providing. They gathered in the cups of their hands at first. Then they collected in a rolled up leaf— much like the *tatsa*. Then eventually they moved to baskets like this. In the old days women used this daily for work. Now we use it in ceremony."

He took the *tatsa* from me and held it up so that the fringe dangled around my face. Suddenly the cones were all around me jingling. It was strangely calming and peaceful. The fringe tickled my head and face.

"In the Sunrise ceremony we use it to pour corn over the girl's head so that their family will always have food."

"Ah, it's coming on. Watch." He sat back on the couch. I did too. I couldn't believe I would just have the day off on the couch. The film started and the title came up: *Hombre*, starring Paul Newman.

"Elmore Leonard wrote lots of good Westerns. Martin Ritt directed. This is not a John Wayne picture with fake Indians and stylized bar fights. I advised on this picture. Martin wanted to get a real *Ndee* perspective in it. That is what I want you to see. It was made here too at Old Tucson. This film helped make Newman a star. Very good man, Newman. Been married forever. And only twice."

The movie got underway. I had to split my attention between grandfather's remarks and following the plot line. Usually he would wait till a commercial to interject, but not always. Some scene or person would trigger a memory and he was eager to tell me of it.

Newman was, as always, too cool, even as a white man with long hair raised by Apaches from boyhood. In the story he inherits property from his dead white father. So he cuts his hair and takes a stagecoach back to Tucson after selling his house.

The first scene Phillip got excited about and pointed out was Newman in the stage station, waiting for the coach. He meets his fellow passengers, who include among others a feisty woman who ran his boarding house, and the Indian agent from San Carlos who is running off with money he has stolen by starving the Apaches. Darin McGavin plays a soldier who is just getting out of the Army and going to meet his new mail-order bride back East.

Then in walks Richard Boone, consummate bad guy, who wants to get a ticket on the stage so as to act as the inside man on the hold-up. But no seats are left. Boone goes over to Newman and tries to bully Newman into giving him his ticket.

Of course it doesn't work. But McGavin, the soldier, intervenes trying to help Newman. Boone, the epitome of the evil bad man, refocuses his efforts now on McGavin, and successfully intimidates him into giving up his ticket. In the end McGavin hands over his ticket to Boone and leaves humiliated. Boone goes outside for a smoke. That leaves Newman sitting near his fired boardinghouse woman.

"That soldier would've helped you. You should have helped him," she accuses.

"I didn't ask for his help," Newman replies laconically.

"He didn't even have a gun," she counters.

"Well, if he doesn't want to carry one, that's his business," Newman answers.

"Takes quite a bit to light a fire under you, doesn't it?" She looks at him.

Then Newman replies. "You lookin' to find out?" A commercial intervened as Phillip began talking excitedly.

"Now see how Newman interacts in a totally Apache way. He does not back down from Boone but neither does he help McGavin, because he did not ask for help, that is, he did not indebt himself through *shi'take'e*. And when the lady points out that the soldier did not even have a gun, Newman says 'that's his choice,' meaning no one tells another what to do—free men are on their own." He nods happily. "Pure Apache thought process. And that was woman nagging. Just like Lil does. Never works on men."

The movie came back on. The stage is later held up by a gang that Newman engages with trademark Apache efficiency, killing several of the robbers. But the agent's wife leaves her husband voluntarily for the gang's leader. While she rides off with Richard Boone, Newman heads off across country on foot with the stage coach passengers in tow. But not the corrupt Indian agent.

Phillip interpreted again. "See how Newman punishes the agent in a typical Apache fashion. He banishes him from the group, puts him outside the circle, to make the trek out of the desert on his own."

The film continues as Newman leads the group to an abandoned building in a ghost town on a hilltop to rest and await nightfall.

The agent staggers in almost dead from the heat and dehydration. Newman orders everyone to remain hidden because he knows the bandits are out there looking for them, the money and their even more precious water. The feisty woman, always butting heads with Newman, ignores his warning and yells down to the agent, giving their position away. Sure enough, the three remaining bandits ride in and surround them. They want to exchange the agent's wife for the money and water.

They stake the agent's wife in the sun, and wait. She screams for hours, but then as the Arizona summer sun begins to literally cook her alive, her cries for help begin to fade.

"Now pay attention, *shiye'e,*" Phillip said, jostling me with his elbow. "This is the finale."

The cries from the dying agent's wife fade with her life. Another woman in the stagecoach party says, "Isn't anyone going to do anything?"

So Newman tosses the saddlebags stuffed with the stolen money out into the middle of the floor, and says, "Anybody want to take them down there?"

Phillip interrupted, "He does that because a woman has asked for his service due her as a woman. In Apache tradition it is the women who say the fierce or angry words that drive the men to war. Because when your women tell you to fight, it is probably time to do so."

"Because he is a man and warrior and must put himself between innocence and evil?" I asked.

"Yes, but she is not innocent. Remember, the agent's wife chose to go with the bandits. Listen." Phillip pointed his chin at the TV.

Newman points his chin at the agent. "That's his woman down there. But he doesn't care enough about his own woman, so maybe somebody else does. Mendez, Billy Lee—what's your last name, you want to go down there, what about you?" He questions the young woman who had started the controversy. "But there's just one thing, whoever goes down there isn't coming back. They'll shoot you."

"You're telling us that so we won't go down," the young woman interjects.

"I'm telling you because they'll shoot you," Newman retorts dryly.

"Phillip spoke over Newman excitedly. "See how he goes around the room by rank of *shi'take'e,* from the eldest man who bears the most responsibility to the youngest woman who bears the least."

No one reaches for the saddlebags. Then after a long beat, the red-haired lady stands up, screws up her courage and walks over to the bags. She picks them up and throws them over her shoulder. Then she walks slowly over to Newman and says, "Give me your knife. That's all I want from you."

After an even longer beat, Newman reaches out for the saddle-bags and utters the immortal line, "You want a lot more than that from me, lady."

Stunned, she hands him the saddle bags. He removes the money and replaces them with rags. "Come here, kid," he orders the young Billy Lee. "I'm not looking to get myself killed, so listen close. When I go down there, the Mexican will come out behind me. If he touches his gun, shoot him." Newman hands him his Winchester.

"In the back?" Billy asks.

"I'll ask him to turn around," Newman replies laconically "About the money though. Maybe it's you who will have to take it back to San Carlos. I owe it. I hunted every foot of that land up there. So maybe it's you who will have to return it."

"But we thought you were going to keep it," Billy exclaims "We all did."

Newman says deadpan, "You think what you want." He turns back to Billy one last time. "Tell 'em to cut you out a plain, ten dollar horse, proper way of thanks." And he heads down the hill to three-against-one combat.

In the finale, Newman faces down the three bandits, frees the agent's wife, and ultimately dies—but only after killing all three of the bad guys. The final frame superimposes Newman's death face over an old tin-type photo of a young white boy surrounded by long-haired Apache kids. Like Newman himself and all of his films, it was a sophisticated, subtle and classy story, well told and well acted.

Phillip turned to me on the couch. "So why does Newman act when the woman asks him, but not when the soldier does?"

"Because he has no burden to the soldier, but as a man and a warrior he has an obligation to the woman." I guess.

"Yes, *ow,* but there is more. She shames him. He asks if anyone is willing to rescue the agent's wife, and she stands up. She is willing to act in his role as a warrior when he will not, so his self-image as an Apache man and warrior, the core of his being, is challenged, and because of upbringing, he must answer that challenge. And he does." He shakes his head.

"We men will die rather than be shamed by women. But nowadays all women know how to do is nag like Lilith, and that never works. You find a woman that'll shame you instead of nag you, and you'll be a lucky man."

"Did you?"

"A long time ago."

"Your wife?" I asked. Phillip gave me a disapproving look and only silence. I knew I had stepped over the line. "What about the money?" I reminded him.

"Ah, that's a good point. He wants the money returned because of his *shit'akee* to his adopted people, the Apache up on San Carlos reservation. Remember, he says, 'I owe it.' He is so defined by his duty inside his Apache hoop that he is even concerned about fulfilling it *after* his death. He even tells the boy to ask for a horse, so that the one he sends to represent him in death is seen as properly mannered. He is a true Apache, consumed by his sense of duty to those he is interwoven with. And how is it today? Where is the sense of personal duty?"

"Non-existent," I said.

"And do people live together in circle, guarding each other's flanks with their children all together in the center? Is that how yards are today?"

"Just the opposite," I said. "Modern, pop culture is where everyone's back yard is fenced off from the other, and everyone's lives are separated, isolated out from each other, where you don't even know your neighbor."

"So…this film is probably the best example of the Apache manhood and warriorship way of impeccability ever made," Phillip mused.

He had again surprised me. I never would have thought that we would sit on the couch at his place and just watch TV for training, but we did this later on many occasions and on many subjects. And always he would be questioning me and prompting me, and pointing out the subtleties of teaching throughout the film.

"You know, I could tell you Apache stories, but they are difficult to translate. We call those shooting arrows. Stories shot at certain people at certain times to teach certain points. Many times an Apache cowboy, he just rides along the fence-line up there and he'll sing place names. Like, 'It happened up there at white rocks.' And that means an uncle raped his niece up there a long time ago."

He paused remembering and continued. "And the father, he killed that uncle with a rock. And because that crime was so bad, they just let the body lay unburied up there. And when that cowboy says that place name, well he knows that story and that story teaches him a lesson and that lesson keeps him straight. That's how the land keeps us on the red road."

"What about coyote stories?" I asked. I had heard about them among many other tribes, but I didn't know if the Apache had them as well.

"Yes, we have stories of Coyote, the fire stealer, that teach us lessons. And we have a subtle way of elder teaching called shooting arrows, at youth, special coded stories designed to touch someone specifically. And we have sayings too."

"Sayings. Like what?"

"Um...." He thought for a moment, then smiled and said, "Like little boys are lightning and little girls are butterflies."

"What does that mean?" I knit my brow trying to figure that one out.

"Easy," Phillip shrugged, "Little boys are lightning because you never know where they'll strike next. Little girls are butterflies because they bring goodness wherever they light."

"That's beautiful and true." I said, "But you're right. I never would have got that."

"That's because it's pure Apache."

"But what about coyote stories?"

"Ever heard any?"

"No, only heard of them," I admitted.

"Well, let's see. There's a million of 'em," Phillip looked up and left into his memory. "Ah, yes, well one time old Coyote was braggin' to Rabbit about how he could throw his eyeballs into the air. Rabbit didn't believe him, and told him to prove it. So Coyote, he throws his eyes up in the air and Rabbit, he jumps right in and catches and takes 'em and runs off with 'em, leaving Coyote blind."

I looked at him blankly. "So what the hell does that mean?"

Phillip laughed. "My point exactly."

"One more," I begged. Phillip shook his head.

"All right, one more." He secretly seemed to be enjoying telling these stories as if he didn't get to tell them to the younger generation enough anymore. "Well Coyote, he talked a Navajo into letting him watch his sheep. Even paid him in advance. Well he cut the heads off those sheep and ate 'em as soon as the Navajo left. Then he stuck their heads into that soft mud in the shallows of the river there. Then he ran and got the Navajo and said, 'Sorry but I let your sheep get stuck in the mud, come on.'" Phillip was really into his story now, acting it out as if there was a roomful of kids instead of just one confused white guy.

"So they ran to the river bank and that Navajo was angry. 'You stupid coyote, go to my woman and tell her to give you a shovel, quick.' So Coyote runs up right into that *hogan* and tells the Navajo's woman, 'Your man just said you should give yourself to me right now so you get my power.' But that woman, she didn't believe Coyote. So she went outside and yelled down to the river at her man in the distance. But that Navajo, he was deep in the mud trying to free those sheep heads and busy, so he just yelled back, 'Hurry up, give it to him.' So that woman went back into the *hogan* with Coyote and lifted up her skirts."

Phillip looked at me deadpan. I looked back.

"That's it?"

"That's the story." We looked at each other. I don't remember who smiled first or who laughed first, but in a moment we were both guffawing.

"So these movies, they're my arrows, my coyote stories?" I looked at Phillip.

"Yup. These you can understand and also they are luminous too—they are light on film."

"Wow, that's wild. I hadn't thought of that. Recorded luminosity. Cool!"

Phillip smiled. "This cycle is your adult time. The training here is a mixture of purification and empowerment. You must find the balance between the two. You must now find the impeccable balance of life between physical and spiritual life that puts you just where you need to be, to be of the most use at each moment—the most connected."

"That's profound, *shiwoye*. I'll have to think that one over."

"No, don't think. Feel, dream, and know. Stand up straight, tongue on the roof of your mouth, watch your breathing, and slow your heart. Come back to center in balance, and just know. That's what being a man means, adjusting to life as you need to."

"Know?"

"Skipping the seeing part so that you just know."

"Okay."

"You should also evaluate yourself wherever you are weak and work on that." He paused as if to let me think about that.

"Come back next Friday and tell me where you need to work on yourself to be a better, more impeccable man according to natural law." I stood there waiting for more, but there was no more.

Phillip had, as was his custom, said what he needed to say. He had said it once. He expected me to listen, then be silent as Indians are, and absorb the meaning and subtleties behind his words, to sift out the message, translate it, and then, if it was my choice, act on it. I knew he would not say more, but I stayed put another few moments making sure I had everything straight in my head. It was a lot to absorb.

I slowly nodded to myself, then to Phillip. He nodded back. And I left.

I returned the next Friday. Phillip was sitting outside waiting for me. When I arrived, he waved and headed into my car.

"Where are we going?" I hadn't even turned off the ignition.

"San Xavier Mission School." Phillip pointed with his pursed lips. "South on Nineteen to the San Xavier exit."

"Yes, sir," I replied and put her in gear.

I knew the way. After the Grand Canyon and the Desert Museum, San Xavier is one of the major tourist stops in Arizona. San Xavier *Del Bac* is known as the white dove of the desert. It is a beautiful old mission church built by the *Tohono O'Odaam* Indians and still run by the Franciscans. Its interior has been compared with the Sistine Chapel, but it is probably best known for its unfinished east tower. It even appears on the Tucson city seal.

When we arrived, Phillip directed me not to the chapel but the school next door. We stopped and got out. We must have been expected because a skinny nun in her thirties came out immediately to greet us.

"Oh, thank you so much, *Nantan,* for coming. The children are thrilled," she gushed.

"*Nantan?*" I asked.

"*Ndee* for chief," Phillip said. "Sister Mary Joseph, this is Jeffrey."

"Welcome to San Xavier grade school, Jeffrey. It is a pleasure to have you. This way." The sister was a bundle of infectious positive energy. She turned back to Phillip. "We have been looking forward to your visit all week. It so helps the children to see positive native role models like yourself. I wish we could get more."

"Me too, sister, me too," Phillip replied.

We passed through a chain link gate and headed into a double-wide trailer. Just before entering, I glanced at a strange stone building across the street. Phillip caught me looking. "That's their feast house."

We continued into the building, turned a corner and stepped into a classroom. Fifty little brown Indian kids stood and in chorus said, "*Dagote'ee Nantan* Talgo!"

"We've been practicing all week. How's our *Ndee?*" The sister was beaming with pride.

Phillip beamed back, looked out over the sea of eager faces and said, "Just fine, sister." And then to the class, "*Skug skiernam.* Hello in *O'Odam,*" he whispered to me.

"Now my grandchildren, let me tell you how happy I am to be here with you today. You know, everybody thinks that the Apache are desert people, but really we are mountain people. You are the true desert people, able to live here even in the summer heat because of your ancestors' strength and cleverness. But today many young people do not know their ancestors' ways because they do not know their duties."

One overweight, round brown face up-front raised his hand, "What duties, Grandfather?"

"You know, I was hopin' somebody really smart would ask that exact question. Are you really smart?" Phillip looked at the boy seriously.

The boy nodded affirmatively, looked sideways at his companions for a moment, paused and then shook his head in the negative. A chorus of laughter erupted from his compatriots and after a moment he too laughed. Phillip and the boy grinned at each other like a couple of raccoons.

"Well, I'm not talking about book smart. I'm sure Sister Mary Joseph is doin' a great job of teaching you math and grammar. I'm talking about Indian smart."

"What's Indian smart, Grandfather Talgo?" a tiny girl voice piped.

"Well, you are, granddaughter. You know why?"

The little girl shook her head in the negative.

"Indian smart is always knowing your place in the hoop and web of life. And knowing your duty. You know your duty because you called me by my duty name, 'Grandfather.' That means I'm an elder and it's my duty to teach you. And what's your duty, class?"

"To listen," said one little girl.

"And learn!" cried another.

"From our elders. From those who have gone before and shown us the way," finished Sister Mary Joseph.

"*Enju.* Well now, we are going to practice our duties. But not in the classroom. Sister, is it all right if we head outside?" The class erupted again in a sea of "pleases."

"Of course it is," Sister Mary Joseph responded. "All right, class, stand up."

After several false starts and bathroom breaks we made it outside into a primitive dirt playground with basketball backboards and a jungle gym as the lone equipment. A couple of pine trees dotted the corners of the field which ran leisurely downhill into a dry wash. There was no fence.

"*Shiyee,* while the kids are filing out, go gather pine cones over there," Phillip ordered. I went off. The first kids to emerge joined me, industriously picking up pine cones. We got a bunch and headed back to Phillip.

"That's fine. Now, we're going to play a game that Apache kids used to play in the old days."

"Yay!" We got a loud cheer from the midgets.

"It's called Hunt Game. It's lot of fun, and teaches everyone's duties, and everyone's place in the hoop. We're going to need a bunch of different animals. Now who wants to be wolves?"

Another chorus ensued as a dozen little hands shot up in the air. Phillip chose ten wolves, two packs of five.

"Now you packs have to choose an alpha wolf, male or female, and you hunt together and do everything together and you talk by howls, and can trot everywhere. But to kill prey, two wolves have to put both hands on their prey." Phillip demonstrated by placing both his hands palms down on my back. Immediately a howling ensued from the wild bunch.

"Who wants to be panthers?" Another chorus went up but this time of growls, snarls and from somewhere a purr. Phillip chose four kids to be cats.

"Now the cats hunt together in pairs, but they are quiet. They can run four paces and one cat puts two hands on prey to kill it." Those kids immediately became cats and started slinking around.

"Now I need two bears, but they hunt alone, and one puts one hand on any prey to kill it. But they can only walk. Sometimes they'll just sleep and sometimes they walk right up and help defend people, and sometimes they'll just kill 'em." Two volunteers immediately went into bear mode.

"And now I need a family, who wants to be the dad?"

"I will!" yelled one husky little guy. Phillip picked him and he fell silent but smiled broadly.

"And who wants to be the mom?"

"I do, I do," a little girl clutching a beat-up doll raised her hand and jumped up and down. Phillip picked the little girl and she was all smiles.

"And lastly I need a child." Phillip tapped the remaining little girl on the head. "That's you." She beamed up at him. "Now listen, my grandchildren. Pretend it is Ghost Face, winter time in the old time. The vegetation is all gone. The deer have stood up on their hind legs and eaten all the bark off the trees. Then they left. Now only the predators remain. And since there is no prey left, the predators, they are hunting each other."

Squeals from the girls and shouts from the boys erupted!

"Now the nation has broken up into tribes, and the tribes into clans and the clans into bands and finally, because the land will not even support that, individual family units." He looked down at the tiny threesome. "That means you." They nodded gravely up at Phillip fully assuming their roles and the weight of their responsibilities.

"This family has to go out, hunt something with these pine cone arrows, and bring it back here to me to their lodge." More squeals and shouts ensued. "And all without losing any family members."

"What do you mean losing?" A tiny voice from the crowd.

"I mean losing your life to a predator. Being eaten by the lion, bears or wolves." Phillip grinned and the children grinned back.

"Cool," another dusty little boy chimed in.

"Now it takes one pine cone to kill a wolf, two for a lion and three for a bear. And remember, it takes two wolves' two hands each on a person or anything to kill them, two hands of one lion, and one hand of one bear to make a kill. Now I know that's a little complicated, but that's okay because you are all so smart!" A cheer went up.

"Now off with the wolves." The wolves trotted off.

After a couple moments, Phillip said, "Now the lions." Off slinked the cats.

"Now the bears." They waddled off, but being bears, didn't go far before they started rubbing their backs against each other.

"Now the family, but don't forget your pine cones." Phillip nodded and I handed over three cones.

"Wait a minute now, you're not going to give your baby pine cone arrows, are you?" Phillip stared, and after a moment the mom grabbed the cones from the kid. "Okay, off with you. Don't come back till you kill something."

The family trudged off into the field. In short order the wolves surrounded them. First they picked off the child, then the mom, and soon after the dad. For good measure the lions killed a wolf. But the bears were nowhere to be found. A happy, general chaos quickly ensued, until the bears finally wandered back in and, not realizing the game was over, started pawing everyone in sight saying, "Graah!"

"Okay, everyone come on back in," Phillip called. The tribe closed in. "Quiet down. Now what happened?" A dozen little voices chimed in at once. "Okay, now what happened to the baby?"

"We got her," the wolves chimed in.

"So who should have been protecting the baby?" Phillip asked the little crowd.

"The mom is supposed to take care of the baby," a young girlish voice from the crowd chimed in.

"But then if the mom is watching over the baby, who is protecting the mom?" Phillip looked out over the crowd.

"The dad, the dad's gotta protect the mom, so she can protect the baby," another youngster spat out.

"Yeah, that's right," another half-pint agreed.

"So what was your plan?" Phillip queried the former family.

They squirmed and then said, "We didn't have one."

"What was your job?" Phillip asked.

"Huh?" said one half-pint.

"The homework assignment. What was it?" Sister Mary interpreted.

"Hunt something," one of the boys piped up.

"Yeah, one of the predators," a tall skinny girl added.

"Well, whose job is it to hunt?" Phillip coaxed.

"The dad's."

"And if the job is the hunt, then who is the leader of the hunt?"

"The dad!" the voices chimed.

"Then who has to lead the hunt and be in charge?"

"The dad."

"But if something happens to the dad, if the wolves get him, then who is in charge?"

"The mom, the baby can't be!"

"And what's the baby's job?" Phillip looked around at the silent faces staring up at him.

"The baby's job is just to be a baby!" the boy cried out.

"But can he do that if he is panther food or eaten by wolves?" Phillip asked.

"Nooo!" chimed a chorus.

"Then what's his job?" Phillip pointed to a little girl with a raised hand.

"To grow up," she said.

"That's right, just to survive. The most important job of all. The survival of the baby ensures the survival of our Indian people."

"We're ready to try again, Grandfather!" the boy dad said to Phillip earnestly. Phillip nodded.

"Okay, but let's change roles and trade places." Phillip recast everyone. Wolves became lions. Lions turned into bears and bear became humans. Then Phillip threw everyone for a loop.

"Now what's your name, little lady?" Phillip asked.

"Eva," she replied.

"Okay, Eva, you're the new dad," Phillip ordered.

"Huh?" Eva was too startled to say anything else.

"And you, youngster, what's your name?"

"Michael." He was missing a tooth.

"Well, Michael, you are the new mom," Phillip ordained. A torrent of whoops and whistles issued forth. Michael grinned broadly and primped his hair. A trio of his buddies hooted and hollered.

"All right, settle down. Now who wants to be the child?" Phillip looked over the crowd and picked out a small boy. "And you are now the baby girl. What's your name, Adam?"

"No, it's Jake," a small voice filtered up to us from the ragged bunch below.

"Well, that's a relief." Phillip turned and winked at me. "Now can you pretend to be a little girl baby?"

"Goo goo," the little boy deadpanned with a straight face.

Phillip sent the various animals off group by group. Then finally it was the family's turn.

"Off with you!" Phillip said.

"Aren't you going to wish us luck?" the little girl dad asked.

"Luck comes from planning," Phillip responded.

"What'd he say?" asked the mom boy.

"Who knows. Let's go. Come on." The girl dad grabbed the mom boy's hand and dragged him off.

Phillip restarted the scenario. But this time the little family stayed close. The mom clutched the baby and placed him in between him and the dad. The small dad led her family bravely. The little mom stayed tight behind his husband but facing the opposite way, covering her back.

When the first wolf came too close, the dad cried out, "Shoot!" The wife threw pine cones with both hands in opposite directions, scattering the closing pack. Simultaneously the dad targeted the nearest wolf, throwing repeatedly at the wolf and getting him on the third pine cone. The wolf boy howled and fell down dead with a dramatic flair.

"Again!" The dad yelled out. Immediately the wife threw cones again in opposite directions to scatter the circling pack. The little dad pulled his family over to the now still wolf boy, grabbing him and hauling him along with his family back to Phillip. The family looked at him beaming. And Phillip beamed back. Everybody closed in around him laughing and cheering.

"Well done, my grandchildren, well done. Now that is Indian smart. Everybody knowing their duties and everybody doing their duties. Together. And together you can accomplish miracles."

There was a cheer followed by a lot of jumping up and down. The lions growled and the wolves howled and a couple of bears roared convincingly.

"Settle down, class. Let Mr. Talgo speak," Sister Mary broke in. The din died away.

"Thank you, sister. Okay now, was that fun?" Phillip asked.

"Yeah!" roared the crowd.

"Well, good. But did you learn anything?" Phillip looked around the circle. "How about you, Eva, was it easy being the dad?"

"Oh my, no. I think it's the hardest thing I've ever done," Eva exclaimed, rolling her eyes. "I mean you are trying to lead the way and plan everything and watch everybody at the same time."

"So do you have better appreciation for your dad now?" Phillip asked. But Eva was silent and just looked down.

Sister Mary Joseph put a hand on Phillip's arm and whispered, "Um, Eva's dad isn't around." Phillip's face fell.

"So why is the dad in charge and out front? Why does he walk ahead, Eva?" Phillip gently put a finger under her chin and raised it towards his face.

"I don't know." There were tears in her eyes.

"The dad has to lead his family. And he has to walk ahead to protect them, so that if anything bad happens, he can stop it from getting to the mom and babies. He walks first because he is the most expendable. Understand?"

"Yes, sir," came the teary voice.

"And how was it being the mom?" Phillip asked Michael.

"Really, really hard," Michael said. "I mean my poor mom, now I know how she feels, trying to do so many things at once."

"And Jake, how about you?" Phillip looked down at him.

"I learned I have to help my folks keep me safe. I have to listen to 'em even when I don't want to," Jake answered.

"That's good, Jake. The Hunt Game is to teach you how hard being a man and a woman and even a child is. And that you all have to walk together and work together to make it. Boys, when you are men, you will have to lead and inspire your families, just like our chiefs used to do. And you will all be chiefs of your family. But remember, chief means one who speaks for us and leads us." Phillip looked at the girls.

"Girls, when you are moms and wives, you will have to look after everyone and love everyone: Creator, yourself, your husband and your kids. That's an awful lot of loving and it can wear you out. And because women are so selfless, guess who you stop loving first?"

"Us," said the skinny older girl with the saddest eyes I had ever seen. She had obviously already experienced this lesson first-hand.

"That's right. And once you stop loving yourself, pretty soon you start to stop loving everything else: Husbands next, Creator, finally even children. So you must always take the time to love and care for yourselves first, even though it is your nature to sacrifice yourselves first. You have to reach out and grab that husband father with one strong woman hand and reach out and grab that baby child with the other, and hold them together as a family with the sheer strength of your love." Everyone was silent now. Phillip continued.

"Women are a higher being than men because they create life, just like the Creator. So because they are a higher being than men, they can do more. They can be a warrior or a dad if they need to, but a man cannot do what a woman can do, a man can never have a baby. So girls, as women, your lives will always be harder than men's. You will always have to work harder. You always have and you always will. That is why we Apache have as our most important ceremony to help our girls become women, and prepare them for their hard lives as adult women."

The crowd of kids had fallen silent and the girls in particular were mesmerized by Phillip's words. Nobody complained, nobody whined. I think the girls even stood a little straighter, and the boys looked at them with a bit more respect.

"Boys, when you are men, you will see your women always working harder than you because they are able to do so. But that doesn't mean you should not help them, and you should not ask their wisdom. You have it much easier than that girl does who is carrying water all day and then firewood and watching her baby brother. Right up until that mountain lion shows up, or even more dangerous, a two-legged predator. Then the girl, she runs away with her baby brother, and you all, you must stand your ground." Phillip looked at the boys sternly and they visibly straightened.

"You have less to do most of the time. But when it is your time, you will need all your energy and power and all at once to fight the wolves in all directions, and you must sacrifice yourself without hesitation, as true men and real warriors." The young audience was silent.

"My grandchildren, we no longer live in the old way of our sacred circle. In the old days if a hunter walked into camp with game and he passed a hungry widow or family, he would give away some to each, especially a chief. The greater the man, the more he would give, so that many times by the time he reached his own lodge he would have little or nothing left and he would just walk on back out, still hungry, to hunt in the other direction." Phillip was now surrounded by little ones—totally silent, enraptured little ones. He turned in a circle and eyed them all.

"But grandpa," one little guy with a crew cut who looked as if he had been born for the Marines, raised his hand.

"Yes," Phillip replied.

"How can we prove our bravery now if we cannot be warriors and raid and fight like our ancestors did in the old days? Now it is against the white law."

Crew-cut's sincerity was almost palpable. I looked around and saw the same question in all of their eyes and realized this was the cusp of their culture. Born of warriors and healers, they longed to be that. It was in their DNA. But their way was gone lost to them in the chaos of the conquest of the new world, their world. And I looked back to Phillip, just as they all did, to see if he had the answer.

"You know, that is a great question. I told you you were Indian smart." He looked around slowly at all of them, making careful eye contact with each little human being, not smiling but dead serious.

"Now you all like movies, right?"

The sea of black-haired heads bobbed up and down.

"Good. There is a movie I want you to go home and watch. It's a cowboy movie—you all like cowboys, right?"

The sea of black hair nodded again and this time several cowboy hats went up into the air.

"*Enju*. It's an oldie but a goodie and it's called the *Magnificent Seven*. It's about seven gunfighters who go down into old Mexico and defend a poor farming village against forty bandits."

"Is there lots of shooting?" Crew-cut was on point now.

"Well sure, but that's not the point. The point is this. One night the sons of some of the Mexican farmers, they come to one of the gunfighters, and they say, 'We want to go with you, because our fathers are cowards.' And you know what that gunfighter said?"

Phillip paused for effect. He had them now. The crowd was so silent you could hear the wind blow. In the distance I even heard the faint roar of an 18-wheeler on I-19.

"Well, he grabbed that kid and put him over his knee and spanked him good. Then he stood him up. And he said, 'Don't you ever say that. You think I am brave because I carry a gun? Well your fathers are much braver because they carry responsibility, for you and your mothers. And this responsibility is like a big rock that weighs them down and eventually buries them. Working like a dog every day with no guarantee what will come of it. This is bravery. That's why I never started anything like that. That's why I never will.'"

The yard was silent for a long moment. Phillip turned slowly in clockwise circle, his right hand palm out, his left palm up, and after a moment I realized he was blessing each and every one! And again he spoke with quiet intensity.

"In the old days if one of us had food, we all did. But now, my grandchildren, that hoop is broken and we live in the white world. Now we don't live in a circle. Our yards are all divided up and fenced off. Our children live behind fences and bars, and our meat and our cars are not shared but separate from each other. Now we are poor. Because in our old way our society was designed to raise our children into strong men and women to ensure the line of our people stretched out before and behind us." Phillip looked beyond the kids and into the distance.

"But now we live in the new world. We have to worry about the wolf packs of drug dealers and gangs and junk food salesmen and rap music makers that besiege us at every turn."

"What do you mean, Grandfather," the little girl at Phillip's elbow tugged it.

"I mean, you must have a plan for your families. If you just sit and wait, the wolves of pop culture will surround your family and tear you to pieces, bit by bit. You must stand together, fulfill your duties, and march forward aggressively. Or you will be consumed by the capitalist salesmen of sodas, fast food, gangs and drugs. We cannot go back to the blanket. But we have to move forward on this new road with our old ways. Not just for us. But for the whites as well. They too are lost. They would have starved without our corn, venison and potato. Many of their ways are great. Medicine and electricity are wonderful. But the non-Indians are new here. They do not know their place in the web of life. And they have tried to get us to forget ours." He looked back down at the children.

"We must never let them do that, my grandchildren. Never."

It was amazing to see how this simple game could teach such profound life lessons. I thought for a moment of Indian kids in the old days playing this game over and over, day after day, year after year as they grew, and I could truly see how they could move, work and live together so seamlessly without police or laws.

"Thank you so much, *Nantan* Talgo." Sister Mary Joseph said "I for one will never forget your visit or words of wisdom. And I'm sure neither will the children."

"You are welcome. You are all welcome." He spoke to the now silent crowd.

"Hey, grandfather," a small fry tugged at Phillip's sleeve. He looked down. "What's your name again?" Phillip smiled and then laughed. After a moment so did I and finally so did the sister.

"Remember, the wolf packs of drugs and gangs are much more vicious than the four-legged ones. When you are grown you must remember to keep your children close and fight against the predators of pop culture, who are always trying to divide and disempower you. But as children now, obey your mothers, and mothers obey your husbands, and husbands lead and protect your family with fierceness and impeccability."

It was a golden moment and one I would never forget. When we departed, Phillip was enveloped in a cloud of kids clinging to his long legs and holding several little hands in each of his. He nodded and spoke to each child as he gently disengaged. Every one he addressed as "my grandson" or "my granddaughter." And as we drove away, they stood and waved until we were out of sight. But on the drive back I just couldn't resist. I had to ask.

"Do you really think those kids and that nun understood everything you said?" I looked over at him and he looked back with a smile.

"Do you?"

We drove back in silence as I pondered his question. I dropped Phillip off without further comment, still smarting from his comeback. Next week when I stopped back, I thought he had forgotten all about my ego slip. But I was wrong.

"You know, *shiyee,* I'm still disappointed in your remarks last week," Phillip opened the conversation.

"Oh come on, Grandpa, it wasn't that big a deal, was it?" I complained back. Bad move, that. Phillip shook his head.

"Who is the first rule about?"

"The children."

"And who did we see last week at the school?" Phillip continued the quiz.

"The children, I get it."

"And who is in the second rule?" Phillip was relentless.

"Women."

"And who else was at the school last week?"

"A woman nun, sir. I get it."

"And whom were you thinking of patronizingly last week?"

"The children and the women, sir."

"There is more than enough patronizing of women and children today. Everyone today is spoiled, fat and soft. Both children and women are often rude and disrespectful to their husbands and parents. Both need the discipline and leadership of their men, whether they like it or not and whether it is in style or not. But what they do not need is your patronization of them. When men fail their children and women, as they so often do today, who steps in and lowers themself to do the man's duty?"

"Lower themselves?" I looked at him quizzically.

"Apache and most Indians are matriarchal, lineage passes through the mother. With us, when we marry, the husband goes to live with the wife's family. We do not lose a daughter. We gain a son. So even though we are pure warriors, we hold our women and children, but especially our girl children, in highest esteem. In the now common absence of men, women can lower themselves to act as warriors, providers and disciplinarians. But the women's movement of today is silly. It has women acting like men, a lower species, while degrading their most unique and powerful role."

"Motherhood," I chimed in trying to recover some ground. "But what about the nun. They don't marry and aren't mothers."

"Nuns are the most advanced of the women's society of today. A totally selfless sisterhood, married to Jesus in traditional Native American polygamy style, I might add by the way." We both grinned.

"Mothers to the homeless and abandoned children of the world. What is the greatest thing to happen to the Catholic Church in the last hundred years?"

"Uh?" I was stumped.

"Mother Teresa. Her order of the Sisters of Charity remade the modern face of the church and gave refuge to tens of thousands of the world's most hopeless."

"That's true. I hadn't thought of it like that."

"Now sit down, we are going to watch a war movie, actually *the* war movie, *The Longest Day.*" This time he had a video cassette which he shoved in and turned on.

"I love *The Longest Day,*" I said. And I still do. The movie chronicles the heroic invasion of Normandy on D-Day, June 6, the longest day of the war. It was part of the reason I would later join the Army and then the Airborne and finally the Special Forces.

"Well, since you've seen it already, we'll just go straight to the scene of the highest use of power."

"Cool. Is it the amphibious landing?" I asked eagerly.

"Nope." Phillip turned back from the tape, which he was running forward.

"The Eighty-Second Airborne's parachute jump into *Saint Mer Eglis?*" The Eighty-Second Airborne had night jumped and landed off course in the middle of the German-held town. They were slaughtered. But they went down fighting dragging their chutes behind them and in some instances even shooting on the way down. It was a magnificent moment of unbelievable courage and self-sacrifice in the annals of war.

"No," Phillip said again, still working at the video.

"The Rangers at *Point Du Hoc?*" That had to be it. The Rangers climbing straight up the cliffs under Nazi gunfire from the top—after braving the already dangerous boat landing—was the legendary stuff of World War II.

"Nope," Phillip kept forwarding. Finally he stopped. "Here it is."

He sat back down on the beat-up leather couch next to me. "The French commandos are being pounded. They are trapped and surrounded in this old hotel and heavily wounded. Now watch."

I watched. I remembered the scene vaguely. The French commandos were all wounded badly and nearly out of ammo, but still taking heavy fire. Suddenly down the hill from the convent at the top, a troop of black-habited nuns marched calmly down the hill and right through the middle of the Nazi machine gunfire! Incredibly not one was hit. But that was only the start. The sisters marched right into that hotel.

"The sisters are all registered nurses," the Mother Superior announces flatly to the Commando officer in charge. "Tend to the wounded," she orders.

"But Madame, pardon mother," the Commando leader grabbed the arm of the nun. "We are in the middle of a battle here." The Mother Superior lifts the soldier's hand off her arm as if she was picking up a dirty tissue. Then ignoring the officer's warning she went about her business.

"That," Phillip said, stopping the film and turning to me, "is woman power. Could any man have walked down that road under that gunfire?"

"No, *shiwoye.*" I shook my head.

"Those women had to be braver than men. They had to stand tall as true women and walk, not run, down that hill, unarmed, and expose themselves, not hide, and inspire both sides of those German and French soldiers to be better men and not shoot them. And they did."

"So that's what it means to be full of grace," I said.

"Yes, that is a good, Christian term for impeccable *diyi*—graceful or grace-filled," Phillip agreed.

"That's a true story, isn't it? I mean that really happened. Those nuns really did that."

Phillip nodded assent.

"But the mother superior, the woman healer, she did not obey the warrior man, the commando officer," I looked at him quizzically.

"Healers always rush to rescue no matter the odds or the fire, like the Army medics and Navy corpsmen and the nurses there in the war. They will always sacrifice themselves selflessly. They inspire the soldier men to protect them as true warriors by their selfless sacrifice."

"Soldiers and warriors—aren't they the same thing?" I asked.

"No. *Nalgonkaishe* is warrior in *Ndee. Silada* from the Spanish *soldado* is soldier. The two words are not even close. Neither are their meanings. Soldiers are just around other men. And men no around women and children quickly become brutish. Warriors are always around children and women, because that is their purpose to guard and protect them."

Years later, when I served in Seventh Special Forces through out Central America, I would run across those nuns. I had a .45 on my hip, they a rosary. I would remember Phillip's words, and have no doubt between the two of us, who was the braver.

"The greater the man, the more he would give,
so that many times by the time he reached
his own lodge he would have little or nothing left,
and he would just walk on back out, still hungry,
to hunt in the other direction."

No, you don't get to just watch movies.

Stand where you can see some mountains or trees against a clear sky.

Refocus into soft, peripheral luminous vision.

See the luminosity of the trees pop into view.

Now look at the space in between the tree limbs and branches.

Follow those out.

Where do those lines go?

Do some of those lines cross?

What do those lines mean?

If you've got kids, you can play Hunt Game, they love it.

If you don't, now you can go watch Hombre and Longest Day.

PILLAR OF FIRE

*They had war dances at night before battle...keeping time
with the drum, ducking...and moving with their shield...
people would say that you could hardly see them...*
                                                    —Allan Houser

WE HAD JUST FINISHED BREAKFAST at the Silver Saddle. It was an old
time Tucson steakhouse, with a dark wood interior. Worn leather
saddles and tack scattered throughout. True to its name, silver
adorned much of the tack and glinted brightly in the lamplight.

"Wow, that silver really shines," I commented.

"Nothing reflects light like silver," Phillip replied and held up
his wrist. On it was a heavy silver cuff bracelet.

I paid the bill as usual, my debt for Phillip's instruction.

"So what do you need to work on to be a more impeccable,
spiritually adult man?"

"Well, that's the funny thing, grandpa. I just couldn't come
up with anything. I think I'm pretty much perfect. I mean you did
such a great job training me—"

"What!" It wasn't quite a yell but for the first time he had raised
his voice towards me.

"Just kidding. Man, you got no sense of humor," I back
pedaled fast.

"No, you don't," he countered.

"Well, see, that's definitely one of the main things I need to
work on." Thirty years later I'm starting to get there. "Okay, well
no sense of humor, and also I get too angry too easily."

"Yes, less anger, more fierceness. That is a huge problem among boys today. They are easy to anger but have no *hashkale'e*, no fierceness for the fight."

"What fight, grandpa?"

"Whatever the fight is that they should be engaged in. Fighting' for their country in war time. Or fighting to find a way to feed their family. Fighting fiercely against pop culture to raise their children as strong Apache men and women, warriors and healers. Fierceness is intensity for the long struggle. Sometimes a man must endure insult and humiliation to survive for his family and for his people. But if he is overcome with anger, he will just do something rash, maybe kill someone or even get killed. Or get drunk. Today kids have kids and no one knows anything about fierceness, just anger."

He pointed a finger at me. "Anyway, what else do you need to work on?"

"Uh, more patience."

"Okay, a common trait of young boys is impatience. What else?"

The waitress, a cute, doe-eyed young Mexican girl, refilled my coffee cup and added a sweet smile to the service. I paused till she had moved off in her tight waitress uniform, watching her long legs walk away. "Well, I'm awfully horny all the time."

"All young men are like that." Phillip looked in the direction of the girl and smiled. "That is healthy. But you must view your sexuality and desire in a sacred context."

"Sacred, what's sacred about sex?"

"What is not? Do you know the Lakota story of White Buffalo Calf Woman?"

"No, sir, but I'd like to hear it."

"To the Lakota she is like our White Painted Lady. All peoples have a holy lady. That's why the Catholic Church adopted so many of them. What does Catholic mean?"

"Universal. I was raised one."

"*Ow*, and aren't there many sightings of the Lady from Fatima to Guadalupe?"

"She's always showing up."

"My point exactly. But what the church doesn't say is that many times it is the innocents that have the special sight to see her."

"Hey, you mean like us, we have the sight."

"Yes, but don't interrupt. We may not have the innocence to be worthy to receive the vision of the lady. But long ago two Lakota brother warriors saw her. She was shining...."

"Ah, like luminosity!"

"Yes, now stop interrupting. Some say she was naked underneath her long black hair. Anyway one brother had bad thoughts about her and he went to her. A cloud descended around them and when it lifted, the brother was a pile of smoking bones, and snakes writhed among them. Now that is a clear sexual analogy to evil thoughts. But the other brother honored the woman. He gave her his buffalo robe and took her to his lodge and his village. She stayed for four days and then left." He paused as the pretty waitress passed by and we both looked.

"But before she left, she gave that brother the deer leg bone *chanupa*, the first pipe. Then as she walked into the distance, that cloud descended again, and when it lifted she had become a white buffalo calf. They say that when the white buffalo returns, the Indian people and the grass will return. And one was just born in the Midwest, named Miracle. She is now going through all the color changes of the four peoples, white, yellow, red, black and back to white. And now that is why the Lakota and all the Plains Indian people pray with pipes."

He leaned in across the table though and motioned me forward. "But the part they don't talk about now is the sexy part. That for those four days that woman stayed with the good brother. She stayed in his lodge. And he knew her. Just like they say in the Bible. Knowing somebody means sex. Like when they said Joseph did not know Mary before she was with child. Same with White Painted Lady, impregnated by thunder, lightning and rain. That' why her son is called Child Born of Water."

"So knowing means sex, and sex connotes an experience c mystical wisdom," I confirmed.

"Isn't that a great way to describe that union? Are men and women ever closer?

"Besides, what do you think your souls are doing when your bodies are that close?"

"They must be touching luminously too."

"Sophia was the goddess of wisdom. Miriam was a 'Mary,' a *mar* in Latin, a sea of life, and Yeshua's companion, some say his wife. But the Catholic Church and most conventional folks, they always want to remove the sexual component from spiritual teachings no matter what the religion."

"That's 'cause it's old ladies in the pews mostly on Sundays," I joked.

"But true indigenous spirituality, whether it is Lakota or Apache or Israelite, is sexually based. The sweat lodge is like womb. When we come out, it's like birth. Pollen is male fertility, like sperm. The sun dance pole is a symbolic phallus. In the old days they put a man and buffalo rawhide effigy up there with erect members. The Hopi dance with rattlesnakes, another clear phallus analogy, among other things. You will learn much more later about our Sunrise ceremony. But in Ndee it is called 'Na'ii'ees' and means 'now it is flowing,' meaning her cycle."

"Cycle."

"The maiden's moon," Phillip replied.

"So it's all about sex. I love it."

"I thought you would. Sacred sex. The Greeks and Romans were also very sensual sexual cultures. So were the Ndee. But then the missionaries showed up. Only modern America brings Puritanism from the book people that sex and women are bad. Let's go." Phillip slid out of the booth and I struggled to catch up.

"And now pop culture makes sex out to be a totally profane thing. What's the worst curse word?"

"The F-word, I guess," I shrugged.

"But should it be that way? The most sacred act made into a word to describe the most profane?" We walked out front.

Phillip continued. "And what does that profanity get us today? Sex results in destruction through abortion, rape and divorce and abandonment of children today. Disconnection via profaning sex, instead of connecting and creating via sacred sex."

"Why is it like that?"

"People fear the power of the intimacy of the connection because it begins there between humans. Men and women wouldn't even talk to each other if not for it. Today they are totally unprepared for their duties as men and women, mothers and fathers, wives and husbands. Instead of unifying men and women today, sex divides. Because they are no longer initiated into the rites of passage of adulthood. So they fear these relationships because they don't' understand them and are not prepared for them. Even with the best training adulthood and parenthood is a hard road. That is why the church holds the sacrament of marriage as higher than the priesthood. Because family, the sacred trinity, is the building block of the future of civilization."

"George would certainly agree with you," I said. We headed towards my car. On the ground against the wall were two shabbily dressed Indian drunks fighting with each other over a near empty whiskey bottle. They were too involved to notice us. Phillip stopped and looked at me.

"What is our duty here?"

I thought for a moment. "None, *shiwoye*," I said.

"Why not?" His face was a mask.

"They are men and have not asked our help and we have no debt to them."

"We have a debt to all men, but not to help them be better slaves with their own self-imposed whiskey chains," he said and walked away.

"That's hard, grandpa," I said, "even for strangers."

"Impeccability is hard. The Apache way is hard. Grown-up life is very, very hard. And," he paused for a moment, "and, they are not strangers."

Just then a short, balding middle-aged black man in a black Harley Davidson T-shirt bumped into, and bounced right off of Phillip. The red silk bandana that had been wrapped over the top of the man's head had come loose over his eyes, and flustered he hastened to retie it. As the cloth cleared his eyes, there was brief glint of fear I thought I saw, but if it was there, it was quickly replaced with angry indignation.

"Hey fella, watch where you're going there." Comically the little guy had to crane his neck almost straight up to get eye to eye with Phillip. I looked at Phillip. He softened, then even smiled a hair.

"Sorry about that, sir."

"Um, well that's okay, mister," the little guy pulled down on his t-shirt, "you have nice day now."

"You too," Phillip nodded and walked on.

"Me too," I said to him, then hurried to catch up with Phillip's long stride.

"Well, how come you were so nice to him and mean to the Indians?"

Phillip stopped and looked at me. "You talk like an emotional woman. I was compassionate to both. I did not help either cousin enslave themselves further. And the white black man was afraid. That was his act. He wanted to be kind but was afraid to. I gave him the opportunity and he responded."

"How do you know?"

"The bandana was to cover his insecurity about his bald spot."

"What about the biker shirt?"

"Did you see a motorcycle in the lot?"

"No."

"That's why Indians always become quiet around whites. They do not give up their power nor lose their dignity."

We got into my car. As usual Phillip's knees were in his chest.

"Where to?" I asked looking at him and trying not to laugh.

"Back to my place."

"I thought we were going up on the mountain?" I asked, looking over.

"We are. But first, we need to go over one more thing." Phillip looked straight ahead.

"You're the boss," I said turning into traffic. Fifteen minutes later we were back at Phillip's. Inside he handed me a bright red, folded up Pendleton. He folded the squared wool once again into a triangle.

"Sit in warrior seat," he said, and vanished into the back bedroom.

"Start a good breathing cycle?" I yelled after him.

"Yup." Phillip came walking out carrying a long, rectangular mirror—the kind you got at any drugstore.

He set it down in front of me. He moved to draw the shades and shut the door. I knew better than to ask any more questions. I just began my usual cycle of relaxing muscles, slowing breath, then slowing heartbeat, and finally just watching my breathing.

"*Enju.*" Phillip's voice came to me low and steady and from just over my left shoulder. I imagined he was sitting just behind me. "Now open your eyes and pick up your luminosity around your head and shoulders." I opened my eyes but kept my vision soft, unfocused and peripheral. In a moment I had my luminosity in sight.

"Got it," I said.

"Wow, that was fast," Phillip said. "You are the best at this I have ever seen!"

Warmth washed over me at Phillip's compliments. And simultaneously I watched the luminosity about my head and shoulders expand outwards and brighten!

"So that's what the phrase 'swell with pride' means," I said.

"You mean you didn't realize that before? How could you miss something so elemental?" Phillip's voice was no longer complimentary but chiding.

I felt my stomach drop just a little. "Keep seeing," Phillip added. I watched as the luminosity that had just flared around me faded below its normal level.

"That's amazing," I said.

"Okay, *shiyee,* go ahead and relax. We're done." I relaxed and circled down. I leaned back on my palms. Phillip was actually sitting on the kitchen chair. "When you ate up my compliments what happened with your luminosity?"

"It grew. It swelled outward," I said.

"So it got fat?"

"Yes, sir, that's a good way to put it."

"And is being fat healthy?" Phillip asked.

"No, of course not. It causes diabetes and all kinds of health problems."

"And we are well on our way to obesity epidemic in this country, aren't we?" Phillip added.

"We are," I agreed.

"So if it's not healthy or physically balanced to be physically fat, then what about being luminously fat, what about emotional fat? In this generation of victimhood and self-indulgence, is there emotional fat?"

"Sure," I said, "Nobody takes responsibility for their own actions anymore. Everybody blames someone else for their personal faults."

"True enough. But what happened when I chided you?"

"Ah, my luminosity shrank...it grew thin," I replied.

"*Ow.* And that is just what an *Ndee* would say, that your *diyi,* your power, became thin. And is good to be too thin?"

"No, it's probably almost as bad as being too fat. Wait a minute, are we talking physical or spiritual now?"

"Does it matter?" Phillip countered.

"No, I guess not."

"You guess?" Phillip looked skeptically at me.

"No, it doesn't," I said definitely.

"So to be grace or *diyi* filled, to be impeccable, where do you want to be fat or thin, physical or spiritual?" Phillip was coaxing me along. I smiled and put my hand up vertically in front of me or rather in the middle of me.

"That's it? That's your answer?" Phillip asked. But I remained silent. After a moment Phillip nodded.

"Good answer. Let's go." He got up, turned the mirror to the wall and headed for the door. I followed. Outside we got into my car.

"Where to?" I turned to look at him.

"Gates Pass and step on it."

We wound up Speedway through the Saguaro National Monument. All around us giant and ancient saguaro cacti rose to greet the morning sun.

"Can you see and drive?" Phillip asked.

"I'll find out in a second." After a moment the saguaro clicked in luminously.

"Got it."

"*Enju*, now see the saguaro."

"I am."

"Now see above the saguaro."

I relaxed my sight and saw the sky above the saguaro forest. Almost immediately I saw the saguaros' luminosity extending upwards endlessly into the heavens.

"Whoa, the saguaros' luminosity are web lines that go up!"

"How far?"

"I can't tell. They just kind of fade out or I lose sight of them—I'm not sure which." I pulled into the Gate's Pass pull-off and cut the engine. I looked over at Phillip. He was already unlimbering from the Fiat seat. I hopped out and locked up. I looked at him across the low roof.

"Up?"

He nodded. And we moved out. We climbed rapidly in silence. I climbed eagerly wanting to know what this new exercise would bring. Just short of the crest, Phillip turned and put out his hand.

"Stay there, *shiyee*."

He climbed the rest of the way to the rock crest and stood on top outlined by the vibrant brightening blue of the morning sky. He had clearly positioned himself so that it would be easy for me to see his luminosity. For a moment I glimpsed what the early pioneers must have felt when they suddenly spied an Apache on the ridgeline looking down on them.

"See," Phillip called down to me. Obediently the ridgeline the saguaros, and Phillip himself lit up like a Christmas tree. An electric neon line ran around everything.

"*Ow*," I called, realizing that this was a Chiricauhua "yes," and also the perfect, round, open-mouthed sound for carrying over distance. Phillip nodded.

"See my hands and follow the luminosity," he called.

He stood with his legs shoulder-width apart. Then he brought his thumbs and index fingers together over his groin. I thought he was going to show me sun greeting again and that he had forgotten that he had already shown me that. Then I remembered that I was supposed to be seeing his hands, so focused, or rather unfocused my sight there. It did not come as quick as his silhouette's glow, but after maybe a minute, I could distinguish the glow around his hands.

But the glow was greater and more intense at his hands, or more correctly inside his hands. I watched as Phillip inhaled deeply, paused and exhaled. The glow I saw more clearly, increased inside the circle of his hands, until it was a solid ball of incandescent fire there. Then Phillip slowly drew his touching hands up to his belly. Below, Phillip's groin continued to glow brightly. Phillip stopped over his belly, breathed in deeply, paused and slowly exhaled, and now I could hear him singing softly.

Now his belly glowed brightly as his hands moved up slowly over his solar plexus. He repeated the procedure and a ball of light emerged and pulsed there as well. In fact that ball of light over the plexus glowed even brighter than all the others. It looked like a mini-sun, with rays spilling outward in every direction. Below it, the other points glowed, pulsed and rayed as well, like a mini-cosmic line-up of micro stars.

His hands then moved up over his upper chest, then to his throat, in each place leaving a glowing ball in place. I realized finally I was seeing chakras—energy centers of the body. It was quite a light show. Now I could clearly see the line of energy centers pulsing together in time, but the solar plexus glowing brighter and larger than the others.

Phillip's hands separated slowly, followed the contour of each side of his head until his palms rested on top of his head and his touching index fingers pointed straight up. I watched or rather saw closely as his hands came up straight over his head and extended straight up. There was a strong glow in between the space of Phillip's arms. He tilted his head back and exhaled upwards and opened his hands ever so slowly. His arms parted as if on their own until they were shoulder-width apart.

As he did, the most incredible thing happened. The luminosity between his arms flared and stretched skyward in an incandescent column. Then I saw an intersecting luminous column descending from the heavens, like the Holy Spirit! I stared open-mouthed at the column of luminous fire as it silently and seamlessly met and ran one into the other, and blazed like a modern-day Moses lost in the desert.

Phillip continued to sing and the chakras seemed to pulse to the beat of his song. The electric blue column continued skyward until it faded into the deep bright blue of the sky. I don't know how long I stared at that incredible sight: Phillip with an electric glow around him and seven pulses up the centerline of his torso—and above him a flaring, towering, glowing column of incandescent light stretching up into infinity.

Sometime later Phillip turned clockwise, his arms still out-stretched. Then he slowly bowed his head and lowered his arms. The light show faded and I released my gaze. I lowered my head with a groan. My neck was stiff as an old man's. I rubbed the back of my neck.

"Stiff neck?" Phillip was standing right next to me. I started.

"What was that?" I looked at him with new eyes.

"When you know that, you will know where impeccable, natural law comes from."

"From God?" I whispered. But Phillip just smiled.

*"Nobody takes responsibility
for their own actions anymore. Everybody blames
someone else for their personal faults."*

Stand with your legs shoulder-width apart.
Bring your thumbs and index fingers together over your groin.
Inhale slowly and deeply as you draw your hands up to your belly.
Move your hands up slowly over your solar plexus.
Let your hands move up over your upper chest.
Now over your throat.
Trace your hands along the contours of each side of your head until your palms rest on top of your head, index fingers pointed straight up.
Straighten your hands up and over your head and extend them straight up.
Part your arms until they are shoulder-width apart.
Look up.
See.

QUEST

When somebody dies, when you hear the thunder
way over there—so that you hardly hear it—it means
the white cloud is taking him to another world....
When the rain drops on you, they are touching you.
—Phillip Cassadore

"HERE, ON THIS MOUNTAIN TOP THIS NIGHT, or tomorrow night, the boy in you dies. Bury him here. When you return, the man you must become is born." Phillip smudged me with a gray green sage bundle in circles and crosses from my feet to the crown of my head.

I wore my now well broken in *keiban*, faded Levi's and a long-sleeve black shirt and little else. Over the last few months this had emerged as my training uniform. We were in a meadow clearing at the end of a long, dirt road. It must have been a traditional ques site. All round us were the remnants of older sweat lodges, stacked wood and even the poles of an old tipi.

"Turn," he commanded.

I turned clockwise. He smudged my back and stopped as completed my circle and stopped. He circled four times over my head with the smudge, and then tossed it into the fire. I completed my circle and his eyes focused over my heart. I looked there as well. There was a beaded rosette sewn there. I had sewn it myself; researching the patterns to make sure it was authentic Western Apache, bought the beads at a hippie store on Fourth Avenue, and finally sewing it there. In the old, black and white photos of the wild Apache which I studied like some kind of crazed anthropologist, I saw occasional beadwork like this. I looked up at Phillip.

"Made it myself." Silence.

"You know, like Geronimo wore," I said.

"You are not he and he wore silver conchos to better conduct *diyi* through him." His eyes were slits. "Tonight you go to find spiritual power. And you should only take what you need. Why do you need that? What does that do?"

I was silent for a long moment. Then I reached up, tore off the rosette and handed it to him.

"A gift to you, grandfather."

He nodded and pocketed the rosette. Now he took the ever present pollen bundle from around his neck. With his right thumb and index covered in bright yellow *tantin,* he marked a cross and circle over my heart and then thumbed a spot on my right cheek, the man side, for a final blessing.

"I will see you Sunday morn then. Turn." He turned as well and without another word or a look back started down the hill. I went up and into the dark cold night on Mount Graham, *Dzil Tsia Tsia'an.*

As instructed, I began to run. Almost immediately I tripped on a log and hurt my ankle. I realized my mistake and flowed into luminous vision. The full moon already lit the path up the mountain but the luminosity made it almost as bright as day to me.

I also stopped running and followed my benefactor's instruction to power gait. I bent my knees for greater stability on the uneven terrain, leaned forward for momentum and to remove strain from my spine, and pointed with the balls of my feet slightly turned out to best bear the stress of the foot strike. My rawhide-covered feet barely touched the ground as I kicked up, and very quickly I was gliding along the trail up the mountain.

I glanced back. The fire was barely glowing as it began to die. Next to it I could just see the outlines of the sweat lodge. Phillip must have grabbed the blankets off on his way because I could see the bare willow, glowing like yellow luminosity.

The sweat had been short but hot. The hottest of all the sweats had ever done with Phillip. I had sweat alone since he had remained outside to tend the fire and drum. He had brought in four rocks with the pitchfork and I had taken each with the deer antlers. Then after greeting and blessing each rock for each direction and cycle of life, he brought in all the rocks. The heat from the rocks alone had been overpowering. I shrank from it, and since I was by myself, there was plenty of room to move back.

"Pour sixteen times," Phillip called in to me. "Four times four, for the four cycles, directions and aspects of man and *Ulsen*." It was not a request. Now I understood why only quested men could pour water in sweats, because they had poured for themselves in their quest sweat and survived it. The steam shot up from the huge pile of red hot rocks and gushed like a broken steam pipe. I shut my eyes and covered my mouth so I wouldn't inhale the live steam.

"One, two, three, four, and five ..." The lodge disappeared in a hiss of white hot whiteness. "Six, seven, eight, nine, and ten ..." I began to faint.

I lowered my head to the earth, resting my forehead on the earth and trying to find breathable air. "Eleven, twelve, and thirteen...." I couldn't breathe and paused to actually scoop out a small depression in the wet earth. There I finally found a spot that I could breathe in. I kind of tossed the remaining abalone shellfuls of water on the rocks. "Fourteen ...fifteen ...sixteen."

Per Phillip's instructions I had been fasting all week: Monday three meals, Tuesday two, Wednesday, one, Thursday juice and today only water. I was already weak from fasting. Now the steam had taken whatever remaining energy I had retained throughout the week.

"*Tuu*," Phillip called from outside. I sucked on my hollowed out cattail reed hanging from the buckskin cord around my neck. I sucked a good mouthful out of the water jug.

"I got plenty of water, *shiwoye*," I gasped through the thick sheet of hot white steam.

"*Da'a*, no, pour the rest of the bucket on."

I rubbed my shut eyes. I shook my head and took the scratch stick also hanging around my neck and scraped the sweat off my forehead.

"Pour," Phillip called again.

"Okay, okay." Reluctantly I grabbed the bucket and half-heartedly tossed the remaining water on the still glowing rocks. Steam whooshed upwards with a hiss like a living thing. "Aaah!" I grimaced as the live steam hit my naked skin.

"Men don't cry out," Phillip lectured.

"I know, I know, it frightens the women and kids," I yelled out. "But I'm getting third-degree burns in here," I muttered under my breath.

"I heard that," Phillip called.

'Well, sorry, it's just that—I'm melting, I'm melting!" I cried out in my best Wicked Witch of the West voice. Phillip laughed and I managed a weak chuckle.

I smiled as I ran. That had been a golden moment. Phillip and I laughing on each side of the lodge, one last time.

Within the first hour of my run the endorphins kicked in and took away my ankle pain. By the second hour the combination of the sweat and the fast left me near total physical exhaustion and power gait kicked in. It had to, or I would have fallen in a heap out there on the trail.

I no longer noticed my feet touching the ground. I just seemed to glide along a luminous line that pulled me forward from my belly. I saw the luminous lines of the surrounding brush and chaparral reach out and connect with the lines of my own soul and propel me along.

I ran like that for maybe three hours until I was high on the mountain. I thought I would have reached the top but the mountain till stretched out above me. By then, my reckoning by the setting moon told me it was well after midnight. I thought about what Phillip had briefed me on.

"This is your changing time. Your defining moment from boyhood to manhood. Take this brief time to put all your training together, purification by fasting, empowerment by running, and impeccability by moving to the right place on the mountain."

"How will I know the right place?" I asked.

"Know when you see it." Phillip had said rather cryptically.

I had reached a spot from which I could look down and all round for hundreds of miles. I stopped and looked around. Back against the cliff I saw some overhangs that could shelter me when the sun came up. Then I noticed that the ground in the clearing just up from the cliff was shining brightly. At first I thought there might be some kind of reflection from an airplane or something to make the spot so bright. But then I realized that, as Phillip had said, my visual purple rods had kicked in and—combined with my night vision combined with my luminous sight—made everything as if I was wearing night vision. And it was clear that this ground was brighter than the other surrounding terrain.

"Must be the spot," I said to myself.

It was about the size of half of a basketball court. I took out my pollen bundle tied around a second buckskin cord. As Phillip had told me, I found four rocks and placed them at the cardinal directions and blessed each with pollen. Then starting in the east I walked clockwise and placed another rock on top of the first, blessing each in turn with pollen as well. Per Phillip I also sprinkled a little pollen in between the rocks while pointing with my thumb, creating a circle of pollen.

But as I laid my third rocks and pollen circle, I noticed the line of luminosity emerging from my thumb and following the pollen to the ground. I looked at the entire circle and saw a glowing circle much brighter than my yellow sprinkled line of pollen.

"Wow," I said to myself and the night, "This stuff really does work." Profoundly tired in body and spirit, I sat down right there at the west point of my circle, my rock in my lap, and tried to focus on what to do next. I was dead tired and my eyes slowly drifted shut. For whatever random reason I recalled the last video clip Phillip had shown me earlier that morning at his house and just before we had left for the mountain.

"This movie is called *The Mission*. Stars Robert Deniro, who is a devotee of my friend the great medicine man, Fools Crow. Anyway it's back in the seventeen hundreds. Deniro starts out as a slaver for Portugal in the Amazon, killing and enslaving the Indians down there. His soul is darkened and twisted by all this badness and finally he even kills his own brother in a fit of jealous rage over a woman." Phillip slid the tape in and moved back to the couch with me.

"Well, he decides to join the Jesuits to atone for his sins. Ever think about that word 'atonement'? It's actually at-one-ment." H sat down on the couch next to me and as always I felt warmed inside by the reassuring glow of his presence.

"So the Jesuits, they're going way up river to build a mission for the wild free Indians there. And Deniro, he goes along as a new Jesuit priest. But for his penance he drags his full set of armor behind all the way up the mountains and waterfalls and forests."

"Dragging his sins along with him, huh?" I said. Phillip nodded.

"When he gets to the top of the waterfall, on the very top of the mountain, they see Deniro and they know him because he was the one who has hunted them like animals. And the chief there, he sends one of the warriors over to Deniro who has just barely made it up this cliff with that big bag of armor behind him. And that warrior, he comes over to him with his knife in his hand, and he holds up Deniro's head exposing his throat. And guess what that warrior does?" He looked at me. I looked back expectantly but silent.

"That warrior cut that rope and threw that big bag of armor over that waterfall."

"They forgave him?" I asked.

"They forgave him. He came back to them to help and so they accepted his help by forgiving him his sins."

"So the priest went to the Indian for confession?" I asked.

"So he did." Phillip chuckled. "I hadn't thought of it like that. Anyway he comes now into those Indians' *shit'ake'e*. For his forgiveness he is now indebted to them. Well, in a little while the whites carve up that Indian land like whites always do. And they give the mission to the white slavers for Indian slaves."

"Who gives it to whom?" I asked.

"Does it matter? One of the white kings in Europe. But the Indian boy, he dives down into the waterfall and recovers Deniro's word. He cleans off the rust and holds it out for him, to take up the sword for him."

"To protect the boy," I affirm.

"Yes. So the white king's soldiers, they come and kill and fire the village. And Deniro fights for the people, and dies doing so, fulfilling his duty."

"Just like Newman did," I said.

"*Ow*. And in the end the village and mission are gone. Burned down."

"No one left?"

"After the slavers slaughtered the men and raped the women and stole their children, they left. This is the final scene." He hit the play button. "This is why you are questing tonight. Remember this. Because by not training our boys and girls for adulthood, this is what we are doing to our children. So when you are out there tired and cold and doubting the reason you quested and feeling sorry for yourself, you remember this."

The screen burned and in it so did the village. The soldiers finished off the last of the living, even killing priests, demonstrating that once again commerce wins over religion every time. Deniro died valiantly but vainly trying to save a child. Then all was silent. The dead lay atop each other in the final, ultimate act of self-sacrifice and protection. An Indian-made violin floated in the river, a mute testimony to the destroyed adopted culture of the dead Amazon Indians.

Then the doors of the smoldering church slowly opened. A little naked Indian girl, breastless and hairless in her pre-pubescence, emerged. She walked in shock slowly to the river. A dugout canoe sat at the shore, a naked pre-pubescent boy at the helm. Inside were a forlorn gaggle of even smaller naked children. The sole survivors. Seeing the violin, the girl waded over and recovered it. The girl slogged to the canoe and hopped aboard. The boy man warrior father chief set his face in a grim scowl of adulthood responsibility and pushed off, heading upstream into the less dangerous wilds of the jungle to do his ten-year-old best for his child wife and baby children.

For a long time we just stared straight ahead at the blank screen, both of us sobbing silently.

"That," Phillip finally whispered, "is child power. And it should never have to be used."

Staring straight ahead I nodded.

I awoke to see the sunrise cresting distant mountains. I was still sitting in warrior's seat, my fourth and final rock still in my lap. My right hand was still inside my pollen bundle. I withdrew it, and numbly sprinkled a little pollen circle and cross on the last rock, and set it upon the other three. I flexed my numb fingers and grabbed my left foot and pulled it out from under me. It was completely numb. I rapidly massaged it and in a few minutes the blood came rushing back in pins and painful needles.

I stood up and limped to the middle of my circle. I slowly performed sun greeting. I felt the heat and energy surge up my chakras, warming and waking me. I watched as the luminous trail of my fingers faded slowly in the morning sky.

Then per my earlier instructions from Phillip I went to the four cardinal points and the impeccability connection exercise. When I looked straight up and saw, I could see my luminosity flare upwards too. But I couldn't tell how far it went since I was directly underneath it.

I went back to the center of the circle and stood and thought back again to Phillip's instructions. I placed my hands right over left, palms to my solar plexus and began to sing softly to myself. Slowly I let my palms move outward from my plexus, until my arms were extending outwards.

I watched not only the luminous trail of my hands outward but also vertical luminous lines bowing outward from my chest! They thinned as they spread out further and further. I watched as the lines continued to move outwards until they faded into the glare of the sunlight. It was an incredible discovery. Instinctively I moved to the east-most stone and repeated the exercise with similar results. Then I did the same to the south, west and finally north. At each point vertical luminous lines bent ever outwards from my center, spreading and thinning and finally fading into the glare of daylight.

Suddenly I realized it was hours later. I seem to have lost time, as if I had not been present, but either fallen asleep on my feet or entered into a state of no mind and non-thought. I was exhausted and the near noon-day sun was singeing my steam-burned skin.

I moved back to the shade of the overhang and climbed up on a ledge to get out of the sun and into the shade. Even though it was the fall, the Arizona sun was still hot and sharp at altitude. I decided to slow my breathing and heartbeat and then maybe work on my dreaming body exercises. But shortly my eyes became heavier and heavier and I dozed off still sitting.

When I awoke, it was some time in the afternoon. I was a bit disappointed in myself since Phillip had told me not to sleep while on quest. To make up for the naps I decided to go higher for a better and higher view. Phillip had said that the higher I was on the mountain, the clearer and more powerful would be the *diyi* I would experience. I was already well pleased with my visual revelations, but wanted to do even better. I climbed the near vertical cliff to the next level where I discovered a shallow cave with an even better rock overhang.

I sat down in warrior seat at the mouth of the cave and looked out over the vast panorama that stretched out before me. It reminded me of the biblical fast by Jesus and John the Baptist in the desert and mountain wilderness. I also reflected on Phillip's comparison of the desert and mountain Apache with the Israelites. But soon I noticed that there was a strange pungent odor to the spot though. Not a skunk but strong and feral one that I could not place. Maybe something had died nearby.

"Now the Jews like to look back upon themselves as underdogs and slaves but they were not. The Hebrews were what the Egyptians called *Habiru*, nomadic desert warriors, expert in guerilla warfare. Just like the Apache. Abraham, Moses and Joshua were just like Mangas, Cochise and Geronimo—except they slaughtered more women and children than the Apache ever did."

"Where do you get that grandfather?" I asked.

"The book. It's all there right in the Bible."

"It is?"

"It is. The time of the people of the Jews is just like the old west—only much bloodier."

"So you're saying there is a connection between that desert and this one and the Jews and the Apache?"

A deafening roar interrupted my reverie and sent me into the air inches off the ground. The roar reverberated through my body especially my diaphragm just as the drum had only more so. The smell suddenly increased as well. The roar reverberated around the air and through me and echoed off the cave walls.

As it faded, it was replaced with the mesmerizing purring of a big cat. It was everywhere. I suddenly realized that I was very near a mountain lion and its den. I looked up and saw a true cave just visible above my roof ledge. The depth of it faded into darkness. And just for an instant two great eyes flashed brilliant green in the darkness. My stomach dropped and I felt cold fear coarse through my body.

My mouth went dry and my hands wet. I sensed rather than saw a flash of movement and looked back up the cliff. A puff of dust faded from the air. I got the sense that the cat had leapt out somewhere but having seen nothing I had no idea where.

I waited into the afternoon but nothing else happened. I didn't think he would be back but I also did not want to miss him in case he returned. Finally, I decided that it was best to give the cougar his house and move on. I carefully climbed down. When I returned to my circle, I decided I was still way too close to the den and decided to relocate to a new location.

I began to climb up higher. The terrain was now nearly straight up, but there were plenty of trees and rocks to grab on for handholds. I climbed for maybe a half an hour. It was slow going since it was nearly vertical and now, after the week-long fast, the sweat, and the long night before, I was pretty near total exhaustion.

"That," Phillip said, "is the purpose: The ultimate weakening of the physical to access the spiritual. So that one time in your life, before you return to the everyday world to begin your life as a spiritually adult man, you take this weekend, this four-cycle period, two nights and two days, to open up and let *Ulsen's diyi* flow into you and through you, so that you are prepared for the rigors and hardships of life to defend, protect and lead your family and your band. Use this time to the best of your ability. This is your training for spiritual combat. And like they used to tell us in boot camp, 'The more you sweat in training, the less you bleed in war.'"

"What combat?" I had asked.

"So far you have only experienced the good and light side of the spiritual world. But there is a dark side, an evil side. As in the book with the *Habiru* it is the same with the Apache and all indiginous peoples everywhere. There is always spiritual war between good and evil, and it manifests itself in the physical as well. All of mankind's physical wars stem from the spiritual ones."

Abruptly I realized that I was standing on the top in a small clearing maybe the size of an infield baseball diamond. The ground was grass covered and a large four foot granite boulder jutted up like a ship's prow near the center. To me it almost looked like a sun dial stone like at Stonehenge or Machu Pichu, placed for time keeping. I went over and looked it over, but the stone was jagged not carved and free of marking. The place felt good to me anyway though, so I decided this would be my night camp.

I sprinkled pollen in a cross and circle on top the rock and went to the east to start collecting rocks. The sweat and the lodge fire plus the run and climb had kept me fairly warm last night. But tonight I would begin the night stationary except for my vigil round my circle. I tried to remember what Phillip had told me to do first: collect wood or stones first. I decided on the wood. If I couldn't find enough dead standing wood nearby, I might have to relocate so I didn't see any sense in making my circle first. It wasn't long before I realized there was no shortage of wood though and I began to carry and stack it near the calendar stone. I moved in a clockwise circle round the clearing collecting wood. I went around four times further out each time.

At the end of the fourth round I stopped and sat down. I took a swig from my canteen, careful to use my drinking tube, first blowing forward to avoid any splinters as I had been taught, then inhaling. I sat back and closed my eyes just for a moment.

I awoke with a jolt. "CAW!" A huge black crow sat on a limb directly in front and slightly above me. A chill ran through me. The sun was setting and shadows of the forest were long and deep.

I stared at the big black bird and it stared back at me. I definitely got a queasy, unsettling feeling in my stomach.

"NO!" I shouted, pointing at the crow as I had seen Phillip do. After a moment the crow took wing. I picked up my wood and headed back to my circle.

I organized my pile into tinder, kindling and firewood proper. The tinder was crushed up, dry dead grass that I balled up into couple of loose baseball-sized packages. The kindling was straw sized dead, dry wood split down the middle. I scraped out a fire pit area and made a good solid fire ring with stones. Then I went out to collect my four cardinal direction rocks. I made sure these were large and flat like dinner plates so I could pile more on throughout the night as Phillip had taught me the old ones had done when building their altars in the wilderness.

My breath began to mist in front of me and my hands were quite cold by now. I looked up and realized the sun had set. Either I had not noticed the cold the night before or I had climbed to a higher and colder elevation. Or perhaps it was a little of both. I decided to add a little more wood to my pile. I just kind of wandered out of my circle and picked up standing deadwood where I could find it. After my four earlier circles around the area there wasn't much close by. Before I knew it, I had wandered out into the forest where the shadows were dark and deep. I reached down to pick up a dark piece of standing dead wood in front of me when I froze.

It was the crow, staring up at me silently, and I swear, grinning. My stomach dropped and the air chilled around me. My breath frosted out in front of me and I felt fear envelope me like a physical cloud. I stared at the crow and the crow stared at me. Then I slowly shook my head.

"No, nope, nope," I said. I tossed my armful of wood at the crow, turned clockwise and headed back to camp. I never looked back. But strangely the crow never made a sound and I never heard it fly off either.

As soon as I got back to the clearing, I sprinkled pollen, closing my circle four times. Immediately I felt better. But it was quite dark by now. The moon had yet to rise so I decided to get my fire started. I took out one of the two matches Phillip had allowed me. I carefully struck it, held up my tinder and it lit. I carefully set it down under a curved log and I began to add kindling. The fire flared up warming my body and cheering my spirits. I finally dared to look around. No sign of the black demon bird.

The flames rose. I was warmed and comforted. After about an hour I began to feel guilty for being so comfortable and taking so much down time. I got up and moved clockwise around the rocks in my clearing, setting a new rock on each of the previous cardinal rocks and blessing it with crossed pollen. At each cardinal direction rock, I turned clockwise at four sub-points in the circle, opening up and extending my luminous self out four times four.

By the time I completed my first circuit, the moon had risen and my breath was clearly visible with each exhalation. I was tired, cold, and hunger bit at my belly. My head throbbed lightly from altitude and dehydration.

I made my second cycle, my hands stinging now with cold. Frost formed on my moccasins. My toes were wet and freezing. My fingers were numb. The cold bit me to the bone. I sped up my third cycle and began my final and fourth round.

"What are you doing out here anyway?" I whispered to myself angrily. "Phil and Harlyn are probably yukking it up about now that you're out here doing this crazy shit." I stopped in my tracks.

In front of me I heard a loud crashing as if a giant stone was rolling downhill towards me. I peered out into the darkness but could see nothing. The noise became louder. I could not imagine what thing could physically be making that noise. Then it hit me.

"It's not physical." I switched to luminous sight and as I did an enormous black shadow within a shadow towered before me. The light from the fire did not penetrate but rather seemed to disappear at it as if eaten. It was the epitome of darkness. "Eaten eaten light," I whispered to myself.

The shadow was still for a moment. Then I noticed that, like everything else, it too pulsed. Or rather it did the opposite of pulse. It sucked in upon itself and then grew a little bit larger with every mouthful, for want of a better word. With a start I realized it was animate! It reared up before me. At first it seemed to have rough rectangular shape something like a misshapen head and shoulders. Then it morphed into a great billowing sail-like shape dwarfing me and enveloping me. Suddenly I was surrounded by an inky darkness. Not even the fire light was visible. I looked up. The stars too were gone. It was as if I had been locked in a deep freeze locker with the lights out.

"Am I eaten?" I asked myself, but then realized that even though I had mouthed the words, no sound had emerged. The air ionized around me like after a lightning storm and my stomach dropped as if I was on a roller coaster. Fear washed over me like a wave and I began to tremble. My breath frosted out before like I had somehow suddenly found myself in a meat locker. Then I realized—I was the meat!

Wake up, I thought—fear is the soul eater. This started when I whined and felt sorry for myself. That's it! Power plus ego brings evil!

I was proud of myself for figuring out the answer, but just then I realized that I could no longer even make out my own bio-luminescence.

"Grow up, boy. Let go of everything, including fear but especially ego," I heard Phillip's voice echoing in the halls of my mind.

I relaxed my eyelids shut and focused on my breathing. I inhaled deeply, paused, exhaled and let go. My luminosity popped around me just like I had when I had the blanket wrapped around me during empowerment.

I inhaled again, paused and exhaled more slowly. The firelight pierced the darkness around and the stars reappeared reassuring above. I performed another breathing cycle and now the shadow pillowed out over and in front of me, but at least it and I were now separate. I inhaled deeply again and let go of everything: Fear, no fear—I even let go of being cold and stopped trembling. I just let the cold wash over me. I was ready to die there or at least stay here for the rest of my life.

And then the shadow did something strange even for a shadow. It began to shrink. Well, actually it began to fold inwards upon itself—and from all angles. It shrunk, or shriveled up really, like it no longer had anything to feed on, until it hovered in front of me in long, loose figure eights in the air—and then I realized, it was buzzing.

It circled my head five or six times counter-clockwise and then hovered in front of me again. With a jolt I realized it was the biggest horsefly I had ever seen, which was strange because I had never seen any fly about at night. Then as suddenly as it had appeared, it was gone. I backtracked slowly to the fire. Once there, the flames warmed me and the light blinded me to the shadows physical and otherwise beyond its glow.

I sat for the next hour or so warming myself and recovering my nerve. I tried hard not to think about the shadow. Eventually I sat up straight in warrior seat and gradually slowed my breathing and relaxed all extraneous muscles. There was certainly no hurry. I literally had all night. And I was in no hurry to walk my circle anytime soon.

My body outside slowly became completely dead to me. I let go of most of my muscles. Only those I still needed to keep me erect, breathing, and sanitary remained. I watched a mosquito land on the side of my hand and feed for a long time, but I did not feel it.

I slowed my heart next, slower than ever before. I began to feel sluggish and slow but strangely light from the decreased blood flow. With breath and heart slowed I began to watch my breathing. I did this too, slower than ever before, until I was but a swinging door breathing in and out. And then, finally "I" was gone.

Only upon my return to sentience did I realize I had indeed been gone. But I felt serene and powerful. I slowly opened my eyelids from their three-quarters closed posture. The moon was up and full and the field bathed in its brilliant reflected sunlight. Then I realized I was seeing as well and more sharply than ever before. Everything—the trees, the branches, the grass and the rocks glowed with neon incandescent life. In between the towering trunks the volleyball-sized globes of luminosity floated about like soap bubbles.

"*Dwerdums,*" I muttered. Little bright bits of luminosity zipped around the trees too, just like Tinker Bell. "So sprites are real too," I mused.

Ever so slowly I placed my hands over my plexus and then slowly watched as they extended outward. The luminosity around them was bright and sharp. Following them vertical lines bowed and stretched outwards from below my chin to below my groin. I watched as each breath extended and stretched these lines farther outward. As the lines extended out little luminous lights blinked on and off around them like spirit world fireflies. Then extraordinarily, my luminous lines reached and met some lines coming off some low chaparral nearby. I watched in wonder as the lines met, sparked and joined. A bright channel of electric current pulsed back both ways through the lines and I felt a jolt of energy pass through me as well. A feeling of euphoria washed over me and then I drifted off into sleep.

Almost immediately I found myself in a lucid dream still sitting at the fire. The crow sat on the rock. But now it was gigantic and the boulder almost disappeared under its enormous girth. The crow lowered its head to me and opened its giant beak. Its mouth closed with me until I could only see its giant mouth now improbably lined with tiny jagged teeth. I put my left arm out to ward off the monster. The mouth engulfed my arm and I jolted awake.

"NO!" My voice echoed in the morning sunlight.

The sun was well up and slanting beautifully off the barren canyon rock. My fire was white ash. I put my hand out. It was still warm. Then I noticed my arm. There were two rows of red indentations clearly imprinted on my flesh! I touched them and though the skin was not broken there was moistness in the dents, like saliva! I shook my head in wonder. Once again the dreaming world and the physical had crossed and merged indecipherably among each other.

I knew it was Sunday and I was expected back. Phillip had said if I wasn't at the pick-up point by noon, he would come looking for me along my route, and if after another hour he could not find me, he'd call the sheriff's mountain rescue unit in. I stood up and stretched.

"Well that was fun," I muttered to myself.

I greeted the sun then turned in a circle and started the long limb down. The walk down after the climb was even longer and decided to run some of it. Somehow I was no longer tired, but light, happy, strong and free. I ran lightly down the trail eating the

miles up underneath my power gait. I was well into a thought-
less, gliding gait of power when I suddenly pulled up and skidded
abruptly to a stop.

There was a dead bird in the path ahead. "Not you again," I
said. But as I stepped forward, I saw it was not a crow but a dead
great horned owl. I touched its chest. It was still warm. It was
perfect except for damage to the left eye and the left leg, both of
which were slightly gnawed.

"Looks like you took on something a little too big last night,"
I said. Then Phillip's words came back to me.

"On your manhood quest if you open up and let go of the
ego that separates you from *Ulsen,* then you may make contact.
But you cannot make contact with the all powerful unknowable
source of everything. You can't put the ocean in a styrofoam cup.
The cup would be pulverized. So instead a little fingernail of God
touches you and gives you an extra little bit of power for when
things get really tough." He reached down and lightly touched his
index finger to my head.

"What kind of fingernail," I had asked.

"Could be any living thing. A wind, a tree, a rock, an animal,
a dream."

"Or an owl," I said now.

Phillip's words again echoed in my mind. "Whatever it is, if it
comes to you, do not refuse it. Do not do what some of the young
warriors used to do in the old days and reject the initial offer of
power hoping for a better. That is the arrogance of ego. Take
humbly with gratitude whatever *diyi* is gifted you."

"Okay," I said to myself as I reached out and picked the raptor up by its claws. The head bobbed and the wings fell open as
I lifted it. It was huge and magnificent. The wings stretched from
my feet to my shoulders. The feathers were gorgeous shades of
mottled brown and white. The sheer size of the great bird made a
deep impression on me. The raw power and splendor of the great
desert mountain seemed to be embodied literally in the raptor.

I looked around at all the Ponderosa pines stretching upward
all around me. Last night this form had soared silently among
them hunting prey until somehow and suddenly it had become the

hunted. Even in death the owl was regal and exuded a power all its own. I looked the bird over and set it down carefully. I took out my pollen pouch and blessed the owl. Next I opened my Swiss army knife and cut off the tail. I wrapped that carefully in my bandana. I took the body and placed it as high as I could in the fork of a beautiful birch tree. Then I sprinkled that too with pollen. Satisfied I turned in a circle and headed on down the trail.

Another hour later I was at the pick-up point. I did not find Phillip. But I saw his tire prints or someone's from earlier so I started off down the road. The sun was well past noon now and I was rapidly tiring. I reached the second pick-up point and sat down on a fallen log, setting the owl tail down carefully next to me. I sipped water through my reed straw. I was beyond hunger now. My stomach had shrunk and no longer pained me. I sat there basking in the sunshine, warmer due to the lower altitude.

I must have dozed off because suddenly I heard, "S*hiye, shilgon'nt'ee!*" Phillip grabbed me, stood me up and bear-hugged me. "So you are still alive and you haven't turned into a bear," he said.

"No, but I had quite a night, or rather two nights," I replied. "I sure am glad to see you too."

"The boy is dead and the man is born," Phillip intoned somewhat ritually I thought. He withdrew pollen from his neck pouch this time with both thumbs and placed them on either side of the bridge of my nose.

"Open your eyes. Open your ears. Open your heart. Time to be a man." As he spoke he drew the thumbs from my nose bridge under my eyes, over my cheekbones and to my ears. "*Enju.*" He turned me in a circle and he turned as well. "*Ugash*, let's go."

"Thought you'd never ask." I said. I followed Phillip over to his pick-up in slow motion, worked the door, and ever so slowly eased inside. After days on the irregular earth, the uniform smoothness of the seat felt slightly alien and just a little strange.

"Here's some hot stew." Phillip handed me a thermos. It was hot and great. It was delicious. Thirty years later I still remember the first swallow of that stew.

"Delicious. What's in there?" I slurped.

"Venison, hominy and peppers. Apache stew. Traditional homecoming meal. Sorry you got to eat it on the run but we got an appointment."

"Huh?"

"I'll explain later." Phillip started the engine and pulled onto the dirt rod. As we bumped along Phillip said, "Tell me about your quest. Start with the sweat and describe everything. Little details you think might not be important could be. Sometimes new men come back and say nothing happened and then they tell me about all this incredible stuff that happened to them out there."

"You mean you've done this before?"

"Put boys out on the mountain? Sure many times. But," he raised that long brown index finger, "I haven't trained them like you."

"Why not?"

"They were Apache, you're not. Or not much anyway, even though you understand more of the spirit world than anyone else I have ever taught." I was silent for a moment drinking the import of that in.

"How come?"

"Told you before. You have a different duty. A different obligation. More difficult I think, and bigger. Besides four raids to steal cars in Mexico wouldn't go over today too well."

"Come again." I was engulfed in the rich warmth and deliciousness of the stew. I savored every mouthful.

"The old Apache novice way was warfare. You had to go on four raids into Mexico to steal horses. The first time you stayed in the rear and held the war party's horses. You just heard and saw the violence of warfare from a distance. So you get comfortable with the chaos and violence. Then each raid you got closer until on the fourth you were raiding along with your father, brothers, friends and cousins. I guess today we'd be stealing pickups."

"I could use a new car," I grinned. Phillip smiled.

"Get on with it," he ordered.

I recounted the last two days as best I could. Phillip was mostly silent as he drove. I told him about the rocks, the crows, the shadows. And then I got to the point about lost time.

"So where were you in those periods of lost time?"

"I wasn't. I temporarily had no ego, no separation from *Ulsen.*"

"Huh." Phillip smiled at my use of Ndee. "What were those lines?"

"Those had to be the lines of my essence."

"Essence of what?"

"The essence of my sentience. Because when I opened up, they went out. So they are part of what luminously makes me— me."

"And what is that called?"

"That," I looked over at him, "is my soul." Phillip nodded.

"Was it worth the trouble?"

"Ah, what trouble?"

"Now what was that shadow and crow?" Phillip looked at me seriously.

"Don't forget the fly. I've been thinking a lot about that. You said before that I hadn't yet seen the dark or evil side of the spiritual realm. Well I'm pretty sure I have now. But it showed up when I started feeling sorry for myself out there, that I was cold and alone and foolish. But when I dropped my ego and came back to center, it left."

"That was well done." Phillip said.

"So the dark energy feeds off the light, like a black hole sucking in light." Phillip nodded again. I thought about the enormous implications for a moment. "So what's the difference between that thing and a black hole?"

"Did I say there was one? All of the indigenous peoples have always lived by tracking the courses of the heavens and," he paused, "hell."

"But how could it change forms like that from crow to shadow? And was that the same one from Lil's place?"

"Remember our water talk? Ice to mist?"

"To heron pee, hmm." I saw what Phillip meant that the door of enlightenment was beginning to open for me as I experienced the luminous world in its entirety, including its unpleasant areas.

"But how could it reach across worlds and do this?" I thrust out my forearm. The teeth marks were still visible.

"Put this on there." He handed me a bundle of gray green pipe sage. "These worlds are not exclusive of each other. That is simply the lie you have been taught. They are interdependent and in fact two sides of the same coin."

"And there was a dream too, though I guess you could say it was part nightmare."

"Tell me." I retold the dream in as much detail as I could muster, polishing off my stew.

"If the black hole, dark angel, shadow spirit feeds on light, then what does terror feed upon?"

"Terror feeds on fear," I answered.

"And if you are afraid, what would you physically do as a little boy?" Phillip mused in training mode.

"Well, fear makes one turn away, so I guess I might curl up in a ball."

"And if you are curling up around yourself, which direction are you going?"

"Inward. Ah! So turning away makes one disconnect from the One God and his *diyi!*" I exclaimed.

"Very good, and if you can get one to turn away from God and disconnect, then what is left to turn towards?"

"The black hole spirit." I was pleased with myself.

"And if the evil shadow spirit could not get you to turn away in fear physically with the crow manifestation, then where must it then go next?"

"Dreaming!" I had it and was happy that I finally understood what was going on.

"This is your test of warfare for spiritual manhood. But instead of physical warfare and stealing horses, it is a much more dangerous kind of war—spiritual war."

"Why more dangerous?"

"Because, with the one you only lose your life. But with this way you could lose your soul."

"Serious stuff," I said.

"You have no idea," Phillip replied without trace of a smile on his face.

"Then tell me one," I asked. But Phillip remained silent and stone-faced. It was as if I had reached some boundary.

"Please, grandfather," I asked. He turned and looked at me. Finally he spoke.

"These are old stories, and forbidden. So fantastic they called them myths. From the before times. Before Adam and Eve. Told and retold by the record keepers of the covenant keepers."

"Who?" I interrupted.

"The Jews, the Hopis, the Australian Aborigines, and us, the *Ndee diyin.*" Phillip drew a line in the air and I saw its luminosity trail behind it as if to illustrate the long line of human souls. He paused then continued.

"But they tell us why we must fight good against evil and why we are children born of war. The oldest books only hint at these things because they're copies of copies of copies. And as copies they get more and more blurred. But to make a copy of an interpretation, somewhere way back..."

There had to be an original?" I asked. Phillip nodded.

"Yes. Before the beginning was only the One God *Ulsen.* But other gods within *Ulsen* became aware that they were gods. Like when the river goes over rocks and tosses up water droplets over and over at the same spot. Eventually a droplet became self-aware, self-sentient that it was indeed a water droplet and for a moment separate. And in that micro moment of self-awareness and separation, it chose not to return, and all began with the great disconnection."

"Disconnection of what?"

"Of God from God. And in that space, that tiniest of gaps, all space and time exploded into being and creation. And godlets emerged and exploded outward and everywhere in the newly created space. And always beyond were the boundaries of heaven beyond the walls of the universe, ever expanding outward, and beyond that...."

"God himself," I finished.

"It has always been like that since the great disconnection. The creation made the heavens and the earth and the spirits."

"The Big Bang."

"*Ow.* And it began then. The great war. Of spirits, gods, primordial forces."

"Spirits?"

"Those that expanded in light and those that contracted…"

"In darkness," I finished.

Phillip smiled and nodded. "Eventually over the eons, the spinning bodies of spirits contracted in upon themselves pulling in the dust of the cosmos to form planets. Some of the essence of *Ulsen* remained in the earth, reaching outward to the stars and the boundaries of the universe and back to beyond even itself." He paused collecting his thoughts as if remembering these events directly.

"The spirits, some of them were in the earth itself—like the *shima* essence, a remnant of the One God soul. And others came to earth. And then thousands of centuries later they became physical as gods and monsters." He paused again as if to see if I would disagree or scoff. But he had taught me how to listen and be still and I was.

"At first the gods fought each other in the air and sea and the monsters devoured each other alive to increase the terror of their feeding frenzy, so that the spirits, they fed on the energy from the fear. And men trembled and hid. Later some became slaves of the gods in that place of four rivers. But some refused slavery and fled the tyranny of those old gods." He looked through the windshield into the distance of time and space.

"But we refused and were forever marked and fled to wander on our own, but always free."

"And eventually," his eyes were long away and distant, "we even fought the gods themselves."

"Because we knew already that they were not the One God and we refused to bow down. And for it we were nearly exterminated by fire, air, earth and water." His voice was flat and grim and his eyes had a faraway look.

"By natural catastrophe?" I asked.

"Natural catastrophe orchestrated by the gods who controlled the spirits of earth, water, fire and water," he said as if in a trance. "Nearly all humankind wiped out. Nearly, but not quite. And some of us emerged from the caves in the mountains when the great fire and great floods receded. Where the *ga'an* helped and protected us. The gods were gone. Returned to the heavens. But still we had to fight. And so we fought the sons of the sons of the gods, wh were giants and their monsters. And the last of these was Goliath and the dragon."

Something stirred deep within me. Wild and free and ancient and primordial. Despite my weariness, I sat straighter than I ever had before in my life. But Phillip wasn't done.

"And as those old gods had taught us by example, we fought each other and slew each other and enslaved each other and even worshipped the places where the gods had slept."

He shook his head lightly and came out of his reverie. His eyes returned to this world and this time.

"And that is why we fight and enslave and sin one against the other, and why we are children born of war." He looked at me. "And it is why you must fight now."

I was silent for a long while, drinking all of this in. "And that is why we all play Indian. Because we remember our natural freedom as human beings. And the last of these free wild peoples were us—the *Chihinne Ndee*, the Chiricauhua Apache."

"And that is why America inherited that role of individual personal freedom."

"God given, by the One God, not enslaved by the many gods."

"That's why Washington and Lincoln realized that America was the last great hope of freedom for the human race, and remains so today."

Then I thought to tell him about the lion.

"So you literally went into the lion's den like Daniel?" Phillip was back in his old form.

"Well, I hadn't thought of it like that. But yes, sir, essentially. Me and the lion both liked the same spot."

"Panther is a powerful connector to the spiritual realm."

"That's funny you use that term because that was my school yard name, Panther, you know because of Prather—Panther."

"Panther, lion. Painter, cougar, jaguar. They are all names for the changing one, the man-cat. Here look at this."

He handed me a skinny newspaper. The title was *KABUN, the San Carlos Apache News*. In the left corner was a rendering of an Apache high top moccasin.

"Page four, top left," he recited.

I turned to the spot. The title read *ELDER LOST, BEAR TRACKS FOUND.* I scanned the story.

"Well," Phillip was impatient.

"Well, it says here that last week, an old man wandered out of his house into the wilderness and when they tracked him, the tracks turned into bear tracks. I mean this is right next to the weather forecast."

"Probably more accurate," Phillip said wryly. "Jaguar people, panther men are always medicine men—especially way down south."

"I've heard of that among the Mayans and Aztecs," I said.

"Even the Roman warriors wore leopard skins."

"But I hardly even saw this cat."

"So the panther was ready but he remained hidden, crouching, he did not take you. He gifted you your life back. That gift is an exchange of *diyi* from it to you. And only *diyin* get panther power. You are the one I have waited for." Phillip smiled. He seemed more excited and happier than I had ever seen him.

"Panther ready to strike, coiled and crouching. There is a place down on San Carlos called that, Panther Waits. Because it always did, right there. It's a good name and fitting. I am named after an event and a place, the Broken Arrow. Did you know there is a Broken Arrow, Oklahoma? Place names are good names. They teach us lessons and keep us straight, by the arrows they shoot even the broken ones." He laughed at his own name joke.

Phillip loved to play with the subtleties of the Apache language and the nuance of meanings, to enhance their message.

"So what are you saying? That my quest was successful?"

"Without a doubt! Very. You had your first spiritual battle. You did well. You chose in free will not to close off and obey fear and the dark angels and fallen spirits. You ignored them and opened up. Soul connected strong and with free will to the web. Owl take your death and Panther connects you between worlds. Maybe someday as a medicine man. Well done," Phillip paused, "I am proud of you, *shiye'e.*"

I was immediately warmed all over. To this day I marvel at the affect this man had on me. All the cuts, bruises, stiffness and aches, all of the nights' terrors and fears, everything disappeared in an instant, melted away in the warm glow of pride from Phillip's simple message.

"But," he said slowly, "aren't you forgetting the owl?"

My mouth dropped open in thunderstruck awe of Phillip's casual clairvoyance. He took no personal pride whatsoever in his abilities I realized then, because he did not own them as his, but held a transcendent skill gifted by God for him to do his job and accomplish his mission.

Beyond that he had no attachment to them whatsoever. They were a means to an end and nothing more. He could have had a hit TV series or written a book on such stuff and hyped it. But he had no interest in that. Although his abilities were truly amazing and indeed amazed me on a near daily basis, his singularity of purpose was razor sharp and never wavered. His focus was always to pass on his knowledge to those future guardians of civilization and humanity, whether they were Indian or not, and in traditional tribal ways or not.

"How did you know about the owl?"

"I teach you dreamin' body, show you the web, prove to you that we are all related and connected luminously. That it is the great lie of the adversary that we are alone, because we are truly never alone spiritually—and still you ask such questions!" He rolled his eyes in mock disbelief.

"And you were just doing so good too. Ah well, easy come easy go. Now tell me. I know in dreaming that an owl came to you, because I saw it in dreaming. But tell me the circumstances. God is always in the details."

And so I told him, heavy on details. Though truthfully I didn't have that many to tell. He listened in silence and then remained that way for a long time.

"And what gift," he said slowly choosing his words with deliberation, "does the owl nation bring?"

"Well, secret wisdom, hidden knowledge. They can see—through the darkness and murkiness, they fly silently, kinda like the way you just show up. Hey, do you have owl power?" I looked over at Phillip.

He didn't move for a long time. "Sit up straight, open up and dream the answer to your own question."

I did as I was told. Closing my eyes I relaxed immediately because of the high state of physical exhaustion. I almost went to REM sleep. And then suddenly I just knew. It was glaringly obvious. The connection between the three of us was a transparent trinity of power. I knew that some day I would face death before my time and death would take me and return me and twice.

"Like father, like son," I replied finally opening my eyes and turning to him. He nodded slowly and a little bit sadly it seemed.

"Grandfather, have I done something wrong?" I asked finally.

He nodded in the negative. More silence. Then finally, "It's just the price of power and the burden of responsibility." He was silent for a while and then he added, "The price is always high and never what you expect or want. "But," he looked over at me, "it is exactly always what is required."

"Required for what?" I was again totally confused.

"Your job. To complete your mission. Fulfill your *shita'kee.*"

*"Because, with the one you only lose your life.
But with this way you could lose your soul."*

Fast.

One day. Two. A week if you can.

Head out to some wilderness for a night.

*Turn off the cell. But let someone you trust know where you'll
be and where to look for you if you don't come back by a preset
time.*

Parks don't count. The land is too tame.

*Get out where there are no lights. When you can hear the beat
of a bird's wings, you're far enough.*

*Make a fire if it's permissible. Gather enough wood for the
night. And some rocks. Fist-sized is okay.*

Describe a circle. Cornmeal is fine.

Circle up.

Get a good breathing cycle.

Slow it.

Then slow your heart.

Watch your breathing.

Leave yourself behind.

When you return, see.

Hear.

*Try not to sleep, but if you do dream, do your best to remember
and recall your dream afterwards.*

*This may be the only time in your busy life you take one night
out to try and connect with the Divine, so take your time. Be patient. Don't hurry.*

The answer comes where and when you least expect it.

CHANGING

*Power is a mysterious, intangible attribute difficult to explain,
even by one possessing it. It was, even above his courage,
the most valuable attribute of a chief.*

—Daklugie

H<small>E PULLED OFF THE HIGHWAY</small>. We bumped along a dusty dirt road
and jolted over some railroad tracks. Off to the right were several
old silver BIA trailer homes with traditional Apache pine *ramadas*
augmenting them at various angles and places.

"So what's this appointment all about?" I asked.

"Just made it in time." Phillip looked at me, smiled and pointed
with pouted lips. I followed his gaze. Through the trees was an
enormous clearing with a huge bonfire in the center of the clearing.

As we approached and entered the enormous clearing, I saw
a cluster of cars circled pointing inwards like some kind of modern
wagon train. Beyond that was an inner circle of Apache. More
Apache than I had ever seen—or even imagined. We drove close
and I got a better view. Inside the circled cars was the crowd.

And inside the crowd were the *Ga'an*!

I could just see the tops of their fantastic white painted crown
bobbing above the heads of the crowd. The drumming permeated everything. The beat was primordial and powerful. Everyone
moved to it unconsciously. It was the rhythm of mother earth
herself.

And I could hear other sounds as we walked up: the bells, the
drums, the clacking wooden slats and swords hissing through the

air as they cut. Their stomping feet beat the ground with a decisive slap of rawhide on sand and little puffs of dust swirled up as the dancers themselves twisted and twirled like human whirlwinds. Interspersed with all this was a strange shrill—ululating cries pierced the afternoon. The singing. It was wild men's' music, high pitched chanting that filled the air with a physical presence, permeating the very atmosphere with its intensity.

We parked and got out. I followed Phillip. As we approached, people somehow sensed he was there. They would turn and nod or just stare. But somehow they almost all sensed his approaching presence and turned to somehow acknowledge him.

When he reached the crowd, the reaction was even more extraordinary.

The crowd parted for Phillip like the Red Sea for Moses. He strode through the hundreds of people and they moved out of his way as if he were a king. But no one bowed. They were way too free for that. They simply became quiet and deferential. And even though I was a filthy and disheveled white boy, since I was with Phillip, I was politely accepted.

Following in Phillip's wake, I saw that the crowd was gathered in two long lines, by clans I would learn later on. At one end were four gigantic Cottonwood poles painted white, with the top foliage still on. Down along their length they had been stripped and painted white. All four leaned together to from a gigantic teepee. Buckskin cords connected the four poles together at about six foot height and two great black and white eagle feathers dangled from each direction.

A group of about twenty Apache men stood just behind the big tepee. They were singing. Some had little potted water drums. Their drumsticks were shaved and curled branches ending in little loops.

Phillip moved to the front of the group and began singing with the lead singer, a short, longer haired Apache man in a white cowboy hat. Phillip jumped into the song and nodded to him. He returned the nod still singing. Both nodded to each other and sung together. The song was long and intricate with segments of chanting in between where some kind of story was clearly being told in *Ndee*. Beyond them the *ga'an* danced but I could only see their crowns. They were not just white but painted with intricate patterns in pollen yellow, turquoise blue, red, green and black. The song ended abruptly and the silence was palpable.

"*Shiyee*," Phillip called back to me, "Get up here." Not a head in the group turned. "Now."

A little, wizened man next to me in a faded pink snapshirt and beaded ball cap handed me his drum and stick. He looked up at me, grinned and pointed with his chin to the front. I stared at him for a second wondering what I had gotten myself into now. "*Shiyee!*"

"Coming," I called and made my way through the crowd.

Phillip nodded to me. The man in the cowboy hat never looked at me. It was enough that Phillip had called me. I was accepted and welcome in that spot of honor, by the singer and everyone else. The black cowboy hat man began to sing, nodding. Phillip joined him, nodding. Both placed their right hands to their mouths, cupping them to carry the sound. Everyone began singing.

The drum began. Phillip put his hand lightly on my shoulder and began tapping on my shoulder and nodding. I realized he was giving me the beat to follow. He touched the four sides of the drum head indicating where I should strike in a clockwise manner, and I could see tiny yellow pollen stains there. I began to drum and sing. My voice mixed with theirs and rose in a shrill wild song of freedom such as I had never imagined possible.

Then there were the *ga'an*, the human impersonators of the mountain spirits. They were fantastical, other worldly creatures dusted in black charcoal and painted in white clay, sacred geometry on their bare chests, backs, and arms. Gold buckskin kilts with tinkling jingles wrapped their waists down to their long loose *keiban*. Big brass bells jounced on their ankles and around their waists. Their faces were clothed in black for anonymity and elimination of ego. And above them the crowns spread upward and outward in all their amazing magnificence—exactly, I realized in a flash of enlightenment, like physical representations of luminosity!

In their hands they wielded their long white painted swords, swinging and thrusting against invisible and ancient evil spirits, memorializing in movement the eternal war between the immortal and immutable forces of light and darkness. On either side of the clearing the long lines of clansmen and women linked arms and danced forward and back like solemn human waves refracting each off the other.

And up ahead of everyone else, in the center of the great circle, danced a pair of two women: the mother and the sponsor. And in between them, at the naval of this ceremonial world, emerging gloriously from the ritual of her changing, and dancing alone while surrounded by hundreds, was the girl. She for whom it now happens. The one they, the hundreds, had come for. The new, changed woman. The Daughter of the Sunrise. *Izlandelahee*, the White Painted Lady.

Surrounded by hundreds she danced alone in a regal splendor of singular human royalty. The mother of life. Her every move was elegant, slow motion act of beauty and grace that blessed everyone in her vision with the power of womanhood that emanated from her every pore. Swathed in white buckskins and dusted in golden pollen, with a heavy and intricately beaded T necklace hanging down over her heart plexus and womb chakras, and most importantly, the abalone shell of the First Lady tied on her forehead, she emanated all the beauty of every girl ever born to our world, loved by her mother and adored by her father.

When I first glimpsed her as she turned, dancing regally in a circle, the power of her beauty literally stopped me in my tracks. My mouth hung slack. I forgot to drum. Phillip nudged me once, then after a beat again and finally I recovered and reestablished the beat. It wasn't lust. Not like some construction worker eyeing a skirt swishing by. It was an awestruck wonder at what the whole natural potential of a human woman given society's blessing and support could become. It was very simply, the wonder of her.

The last dance was done. The *ga'an* circled the fire and flicked at it four times with their swords and finally danced off, their bells fading into the distance.

The people followed the dance party through the big teepee in the four directions in a long, slow, solemn train, each reaching up and touching the painted cottonwood poles for blessings. A drunk wandered up from somewhere and teetered by the line but no one paid him any heed and in short order he wandered off. The ceremony was over. Colored corn kernel covered the deer skin and blankets on the ground. White clay paint was splattered every where and yellow pollen turned everything a sunny glow. It looked like a ceremonial battlefield.

"Come, *shiyee.*" Phillip was beside me. The little man appeared and took back his drum. He grinned up at me, patted my arm, and disappeared into the crowd. "Let's go get her blessing." Phillip took my arm and moved me forward. "There was no one to see you off, so at least you can be welcomed back. And there is no greater welcome than this."

I turned and realized that the long line of hundreds had formed behind us, or more accurately behind Phillip. I turned back to the front. Just ahead of us on the blankets and in front of the big teepee a receiving line had formed. The mother, the father, the sponsor and another girl—perhaps her sister, formed a long, formal reception party in dignified silence and stillness. And alone at the end, radiant in the beauty and power of newfound womanhood, she stood.

We went down the line clasping each other's hands, shaking them slowly and solemnly, looking deeply into each other's eyes and communicating deep felt emotion without a word. We passed along the entourage. Phillip was warmly greeted and heavily deferred to. I was politely acknowledged. I grasped each extended hand and said thank you and congratulations. And then abruptly we were before her, Phillip and me.

Without any effort her luminosity shone forth in a pure brilliant intensity of feminine energy and power. It was as if the moon had suddenly risen inside her and shined out through her. She glowed everywhere and above her a column of shimmering brilliance rose upward into the sky in a pillar of luminous, incandescent fire.

Phillip turned to me and whispered, "This is Jonell Cochise great, great granddaughter of our chief of chiefs. But today, toda she is *Iz'landelahee,* White Painted Lady, Mother of Life." He turned back to face her, bowed his head and incredibly dropped to one knee before her!

"We come for your blessing," Phillip said with a casual reverence that I was sure came from many years of practice at this very task. I was doubly astounded. First to see the likes of Phillip, to whom I had yet to meet anyone who did not defer with respect at the least and open adoration at the most, kneel at the feet of a teenage girl less than half his age; and second, because he had said "we." Love for that man swept over me like a warm wave and tears welled in my eyes.

The girl was perhaps middle height. Her long, glossy black hair was parted down the middle and draped down her back to her waist. On her crown a small, fluffily, down eagle feather stood upright, and as I saw it, I realized it formed the basis for the luminous column rising above her. At her forehead a rounded and polished abalone shell disk was tied to her hair and hung over her forehead chakra. Later I would learn it was that disc that had received the first cresting rays of the sun, hitting her and changing her to womanhood.

Indeed I would eventually learn that many girls' cycles actually started at that precise moment. Turquoise earrings dangled down from her ears, so that she could better hear the spirit world, I would also later learn. Around her delicate neck a beaded collar in brilliant white, blue, yellow and red twinkled with the reflection off of the cut glass beads that composed it. In the front another vertical beaded tab hung straight down, embodying the same intricate patterns as the horizontal. In the center over her heart hung a silver concho polished to mirror brightness. It occasionally caught the rays of the late afternoon sun and flashed it back brilliantly. I recognized a drinking tube and scratch stick like mine, but other items I did not have.

On the same buckskin cord was a bright yellow scarf with something wrapped inside it. Under this was a fine, beaded net of the same color scheme as the T necklace. With a jolt I realized she was wearing a physical representation of the web over her shoulders.

Her dress was made of gorgeous white brain-tanned buckskin that was so finely tanned it draped over her like silk. It was a two-pieced affair of poncho and skirt. Both were heavily and delicately beaded in the zig zag Apache pattern I recognized as representing the whirlwind. Silver, not tin, cone jingles ran in rows over both the poncho and the skirt and capped the foot-long fringe that flexed and flowed with a life all its own.

Beneath it all were the most beautiful *keiban* I had ever seen. They were so high that they disappeared up under the skirt's long fringe. The snow white toe pieces had silver tiny bells hanging from them. The insteps and up the sides were intricately and delicately beaded in cut glass bead lines that glistened in the sunlight.

In her right hand was a curved yellow cane. A cord ran from the stem to the curved tip. On the cord hung a large brass bell, four black, blue, yellow and white ribbons and two giant black and white eagle feathers with turquoise stones tied to them.

But the beauty of her costume paled next to the innate grandeur of the new woman herself. She stood, cane in her right hand with a subtle natural elegance in sublime simplicity and a solitary completeness.

Her face was burnished bronze. She embodied the classic eyelid fold hiding the upper lid, a fine and delicate hawk nose over lovely arched lips that neither smiled nor frowned but, as would also later learn, always be serene in the chaos of mother hood, wifely duties and the myriad other tasks that only a woman of exception can accomplish on a daily miraculous basis.

Her face was the embodiment of all that is beautiful, mysterious and powerful in womanhood. She was noble not by proclamation, but by a greater power beyond the decisions of mere men. A daughter of Eve, and favored by God, she was a princess.

"*Izland'lahee,* may we have your blessing?" Phillip asked patiently again, looking up at her.

She stared straight ahead into the vast distance of the Western landscape and the setting sun. But even beyond that, she seemed to gaze off into the very infinity of time and space. Her eyes finally returned to a near focus of this world, and flicked down to Phillip

The tips of her mouth turned up ever so slightly. She reached down with her left hand and took Phillip's right in hers.

Ever so slowly she raised him up until he towered over her. But she was not intimidated in the least. In fact just the opposite was true. Here she was the senior and he the junior. The divinity that embodied her in that instant gifted her status beyond any human present.

She focused on Phillip's eyes and, when she finally spoke, it was with an authority and gravitas that belied her tender age.

"Because of you, I am here today, to bless my people. You are welcome. And he with you is welcome. As my great grandfather was—you are. Slayer of Enemies is your father. You are his son. The red road of our ancestors stretches out behind you. And the line of their children stretches out before you. Because of you, we Apache endure. You are our shield and you are our lance. Blessings are upon you."

Phillip bowed his head. There were tears in his eyes. Then she turned to me. Still holding Phillip's hand, she slipped her right hand under the crook of her cane and took my hand in her's as well.

An electric current jolted through me awakening me and enlivening me as never before. The air was ionized as if after a lightning strike and I swear I could smell the sweet scent of a fresh rainfall. The wonder of it held me in thrall. I trembled slightly with the live wire current of her touch.

She looked into me and through me and beyond. Her eyes took on a distant look and I was sure that she was seeing or face lancing with me. For a long beat she looked through me with that faraway gaze. Then she refocused on the near and present, me.

"You too are welcome. Child of Waters is your father. And you are his son. You will stand at the center of the Cross of a new people. The four return and the fifth will emerge. A new line not of blood but spirit will stretch before you. You will be their shield. And you will be their lance. Blessings are upon you."

She released our hands. The current was cut and the trembling eased. Her eyes returned to a faraway place. Phillip moved off to the west. But I was transfixed. He noticed, turned back and gently took my elbow and guided me off.

We walked west out of the circle, past the crowd, and through the cars to the vast open high desert beyond. The sun was just now setting, bathing everything in an ethereal gold light. The mountains glowed in the distance—even without the sight.

"*Shiye'e*, your initiation is complete. The ceremony is ended. The passage made. Now the hard part begins."

"What's that?" I asked still dazed.

"Life. As a man. You are now a whole man, spiritual and physical. You have done everything I asked of you and more." Phillip took his pollen bundle off his neck and put it around mine.

"You have learned all the lessons of manhood that I would have taught to our boys, if they had been interested. Not the old ways. But my new ones. But they did not want to learn. Most preferred gangs, drinking or drugs. A few, like my son Eddie, preferred the road of American education. He went to Harvard. You alone showed up. So I have taught you alone. Not the old Apache way. But a new way. For a new time." He turned to look at me.

"You are the one I was waiting for. And after the Lady's blessing, I know. You are everything I hoped for and more. But there is something else that she did not tell you. But the owl did. And now, I must as well. Because you are my spiritual son."

"What is it, *shiwoye?*" I asked. He was clearly disturbed and conflicted. I could see it in his face. I was confused. Just after praising me, he was now warning me.

"Owl offers secret wisdom, yes. But the price of this path is your life. Owl means death. Every Indian knows this. Owl brings you death. And me too."

"When?" I said, "How?"

"Who knows? But owl has come to me too. And now it comes to you. And always it brings death."

"But why?"

"This has always been the price of bringing *Ulsen's* freedom and light to the people."

"But who exacts it?"

"The people themselves. Those who serve the adversary of the One God. And those who fear the freedom of personal responsibility and power you offer."

"Sounds like that's just about everybody."

"Just about."

"Are you sure?"

"Do you remember the line the Lady spoke of?"

"Yes, grandfather."

"The Baptist, Yeshua the Christos, Lincoln, Mangas, Wochadeklinne, Ghandi, and King—the message is plain. Do you understand?" He looked at me grimly.

"Beheaded, crucified, and shot," I replied.

"That is what it means to be *isnaa' da*, free, and those who fight for freedom in body and soul. The land you stand on now is all that we Apache have left—because we dared to not be slaves. You are a man now. No man tells another what to do. Decide for yourself what your duty is." He looked back out at the sunset, the blood red desert stretched out before us.

"*Shiwoye*, what are you asking of me?" I stared into the distance.

We stood together and looked west. The last red-gold rays of the setting sun lit the land in one final, golden luminescence. The sun slipped behind the mountains. Night had finally fallen. A cold wind swept over us and a sudden chill engulfed me. I felt Phillip's eyes upon me and turned to him. His eyes flashed like a puma's just before it leaps. His reply was instantaneous and unforgettable.

"Everything."

POSTSCRIPT

Next summer break I returned to my parent's house in Cincinnati. I was living at home and working in my dad's factory. We lived on the edge of a nature preserve, surrounded by woods and the animals that live in them. It was not unusual to see deer, raccoon and fox daily.

So when the owl first appeared, I thought nothing of it. It sat at the very top of an enormous dead oak that towered above all of the others, and day after day it remained. Then I realized it was perched every *day*. It was daytime. I began watching the owl.

Finally I realized that it…was watching me. It became a permanent fixture, nearly always in the tree, or swooping silently by my bedroom window, and always during the day—when it should have been asleep.

Then one morning I awoke tasting the remnants of a dream of owl. I opened my bedroom door and walked out onto the porch. The owl sat at the very top of the high, dead tree, staring at me waiting.

Without knowing why, I raised my left arm, palm up. The owl cocked his head to the side. Then he leaned forward, spread his wings and launched directly at me. With one powerful wing flap his glide carried him to me. He braked and settled gracefully onto my arm! His great mass weighed down my arm and his long talon bit into my arm—although I could tell instinctively that it was not trying to break my skin.

Eye to eye, we stared at each other and waited. The owl flew off after a few moments, but not far. Clearly I had not gotten the message, so four days later a second owl showed up. They stayed with me through the summer and became a part of the family. In the fall, first-day-of-school photos of my siblings include, off to one side, two great horns standing gravely alongside.

In the end, I left (for school) before the owls did. By the time I returned at Christmas they were gone. Later I would dream with them and in them and even fly and see from their point of view.

It would be some twenty-five years later before the owls' message would finally be delivered. And by then it would come in such a way that no one could foresee and, if not for witnesses, would defy belief.

But that, as they say, is another story.

AFTERWORD

I FIRST BEGAN WRITING THIS BOOK in September 2007. And when I began it, that is literally typing it into my laptop—it mysteriously vanished. It deleted itself from my computer. When I had just finished it, that is filling in the review of the first draft in November, just coming up on 80,000 words precisely, the word count for a standard book publication, it deleted itself again. You might say that an electromagnetic current got into it.

There are no coincidences and no accidents. The events in this book are true. The characters were or are actual people (although some names have been changed to protect privacy). There is a reason that something caused this book to be deleted at its inception and at its conclusion. There is a reason I was destined to write it. And there is a reason you are reading it.

So now that you have read the book, perhaps you are one of the few to have understood. Maybe you are one of truly few that heed the call. Perhaps you are foolish or perhaps you are brave. Time will tell.

Now, what are you going to do about it?

ABOUT THE AUTHOR

JEFFREY PRATHER is a husband, father, minister, author, film and television actor, artist, and professor. He served his country as a Special Forces soldier, DIA intelligence officer, and DEA special agent. He earned two bachelor's degrees at the University of Arizona in Tucson where he met Phillip. His master's degree is from Ohio State. He is a master martial artist teacher with more than forty years experience. By his own admission, none of his accomplishments was more significant than his apprenticeship with a mystical Apache shaman named Phillip. After Phillip's death in 1988, Prather continued Phillip's teachings via a life-changing seminar series he taught worldwide. Prather lives with his family in Arizona.

10809642R00169

Made in the USA
Charleston, SC
06 January 2012